The Institute of Biology's
Studies in Biology no. 155

Stomata

E. Stephen Martin

B.Sc., Ph.D., M.I.Biol., M.I.Env.Sci.
Head of Biochemistry and Physiology Division,
Plymouth Polytechnic

Maria E. Donkin

B.Sc., Ph.D., Cert. Ed., M.I.Biol.
Research Fellow in Plant Physiology,
Plymouth Polytechnic

R. Andrew Stevens

B.Sc., Ph.D., F.L.S., M.I.Biol.
Lecturer in Plant Biology,
Plymouth Polytechnic

Edward Arnold

First published 1983
by Edward Arnold (Publishers) Limited
41 Bedford Square, London WC1 3DQ

British Library Cataloguing in Publication Data

Martin, E. Stephen
Stomata. – (The Institute of Biology's studies in biology, ISSN 0537-9024; no. 155)
1. Stomata
I. Title II. Donkin, Maria E.
III. Stevens, R. Andrew IV. Series
581.1'21 QK873

ISBN 0-7131-2868-2

Printed and bound in Great Britain at
The Camelot Press Ltd, Southampton

General Preface to the Series

Because it is no longer possible for one textbook to cover the whole field of biology while remaining sufficiently up to date, the Institute of Biology proposed this series so that teachers and students can learn about significant developments. The enthusiastic acceptance of 'Studies in Biology' shows that the books are providing authoritative views of biological topics.

The features of the series include the attention given to methods, the selected list of books for further reading and, wherever possible, suggestions for practical work.

Readers' comments will be welcomed by the Education Officer of the Institute.

1983

Institute of Biology
20 Queensbury Place
London SW7 2DZ

Preface

The stomatal pores on the surfaces of plants are essential ventilating organs. The guard cells which surround these pores are capable of movement, allowing them to open or close to regulate the movement of vital materials between the atmosphere and the interior of the plant. The term guard cell is entirely appropriate since these sensitive, motile cells function to protect or guard the moist underlying tissues from extremes of dehydration.

For over a century the mechanism causing stomatal movements has intrigued many scientists, but it is only relatively recently that aspects of the mechanism have been resolved. In this book we have attempted to cover many of these new and exciting developments, because we are aware that the translation of research results to the classroom can often be an extremely slow process. We are also mindful that many of the currently accepted views presented here are likely to undergo change with the inevitable advance of knowledge.

We wish to express our gratitude to Drs D.N. Price and A.J. Travis for carefully reading the manuscript and for provoking many new ideas. We are grateful to Mrs. S. Eccleston for carefully typing the manuscript. We dedicate this book to Professor Hans Meidner who has always been a source of inspiration in our efforts to unravel the enigma of the stomatal mechanism.

Plymouth, 1983

E.S.M., M.E.D. & R.A.S.

Contents

1 The Structure and Development of Guard Cells

1.1 The origins and distribution of stomata

When plants first began to colonize land, some 400 million years ago, only those which had evolved a hydrophobic waxy outer layer, or cuticle, were able to avoid desiccation. This waxy barrier between the plant and its aerial environment would impede evaporative water loss but could have brought about the early demise of land plants through a diminished supply of photosynthetic substrate (carbon dioxide), unless minute pores or stomata had developed in the epidermis. Stomata allow carbon dioxide in the air to diffuse into the intercellular air spaces of the photosynthetic tissues where it dissolves in the aqueous phase, enabling photosythetic reduction to take place. Unfortunately, as air diffuses into the plant, large amounts of water vapour are simultaneously lost to the atmosphere *via* transpiration through stomatal pores. As evolution progressed, stomata became more versatile and developed the ability to open and close so that the plant could control its own water economy whilst optimizing its photosynthetic capacity. By controlling these two fundamental processes, both of which contribute to the productive efficiency of plants, stomatal movements perform an essential function in the life of plants.

All plants above the evolutionary level of the sporophyte generation of mosses and hornworts, possess stomata. Those of the mosses and hornworts are largely non-functional, those of pteridophytes are not particularly versatile and exhibit rather limited and sluggish movements, but those of gymnosperms and angiosperms are highly versatile and are controlled by a combination of environmental and endogenous responses.

Whilst stomata are most commonly associated with leaves, they can also occur on the inflorescences of gymnosperms and angiosperms, fruits, herbaceous stems, petioles and tendrils. In many angiosperms and gymnosperms, stomata are found on both the *adaxial* (upper) and *abaxial* (lower) leaf surfaces although they are usually more numerous on the abaxial surface. In other angiosperms and gymnosperms, and nearly all ferns stomata only occur on the abaxial epidermis, whilst a few aquatic plants with floating leaves and some xeromorphic grasses have stomata restricted to their adaxial surfaces.

The number and density of stomata are extremely variable even within a single species. Plants growing in the shade have fewer, but larger, stomata than those growing in exposed sunny conditions, whilst plants growing in permanently damp environments have more, but smaller, stomata than those growing in dry habitats. Despite these obvious differences between plants growing under contrasting environmental conditions, the total stomatal pore area is comparatively stable because there is an inverse relationship between stomatal size and density. Differences are found even within a single plant so that lower leaves tend to have larger but less numerous stomata than those of higher insertion.

1.2 The stomatal complex and its development

The degree of stomatal opening or closing is mediated by changes in the shape of the *guard cells* which surround the stomatal pore. There are basically two morphologically different types of guard cells (Fig. 1-1). The most common form is the *elliptic type* in which the guard cell pair are kidney-shaped with the aperture formed between the adpressed concave (ventral) sides of the two cells. The other form is known as the *graminaceous type* since it is restricted to the Glumiflorae (grasses and sedges) and consists of a pair of dumbell-shaped guard cells. Both types of guard cells are surrounded by epidermal cells which may or may not be of a distinctive shape. If the abutting epidermal cells are morphologically indistinguishable from other epidermal cells, they are called *neighbouring cells*, but if they are clearly distinct they are known as *subsidiary cells*. However, their exact identity can only be confirmed after studying their development. The guard cell pair and their associated subsidiary and/or neighbouring cells are collectively referred to as the *stomatal complex* and are typically subtended by a gap in the underlying mesophyll tissue known as the *substomatal chamber* (Fig. 1-3).

During leaf development, the leaf meristem cuts off, amongst other things, *protodermal cells* which eventually mature into epidermal cells. Guard and subsidiary cells, as well as leaf hair and gland cells, do not arise directly from the meristem but are the products of protodermal cells which become secondarily meristematic. Neighbouring cells, unlike subsidiary cells, are simply protodermal cells which become secondarily meristematic. Neighbouring cells, unlike subsidiary cells, are simply protodermal cells which mature in a position abutting onto guard cells. Basically, stomatal complexes can develop in three different ways – agenously, mesogenously, and perigenously. In all cases the guard cells arise from a *stomatal meristemoid* which, in higher plants at least, is itself the smaller product of an asymmetrical protodermal cell division.

Agenous development The stomatal meristemoid divides symmetrically once to form a pair of guard cells. There are no subsidiary cells (Fig. 1-2).

Mesogenous development The stomatal meristemoid divides more than once to produce a guard cell pair and at least one subsidiary cell. The mesogenous subsidiary cell(s) arise from asymmetric division(s) before the meristemoid finally divides symmetrically to form the guard cells (Fig. 1-2).

Perigenous development As in the agenous pathway, the stomatal meristemoid undergoes a single symmetrical division to form the guard cell pair. However, protodermal cells abutting onto the stomatal meristemoid become secondarily meristematic to cut off daughter cell(s) against the

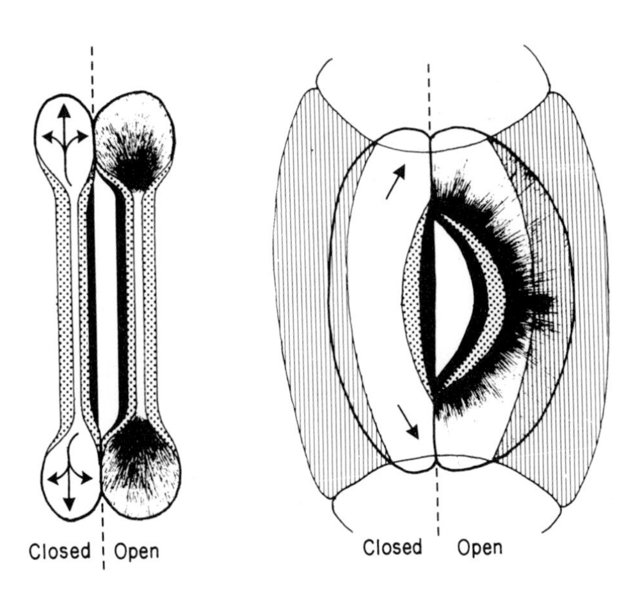

Fig. 1-1 Graminaceous (left) and elliptic (right) guard cell complexes. Stippled areas, cell walls: hatched areas, lateral subsidiary cells; solid black margin of stomata, cuticularized ledges. The arrows in the left half of each figure show the direction of cell expansion/extension which occurs during stomatal opening. The striations in the right half of each figure indicate the orientation of the cell wall micellae.

stomatal meristemoid (Fig. 1-2b,c) before the latter, itself, divides (Fig. 1-2f). Perigenous subsidiary cells develop independently of the stomatal meristemoid.

The number, shape and distribution of subsidiary cells is of considerable importance in the classification of plants, although their functional role is poorly understood. Not all the ontogenetic pathways are found in all the major plant groups. Almost without exception, bryophytes are agenous, pteridophytes are mesogenous or rarely agenous, dicotyledons are either mesogenous or agenous and monocotyledons are either perigenous or agenous. These differences are probably related to the position of the leaf meristem which is typically basal in monocotyledons and apical and lateral in most other plant groups. As a result, monocotyledon protodermal cells are cut off in longitudinal files and the stomatal meristemoid arises at the centre of a cruciform of four protodermal cells (Fig. 1-2). This ordered arrangement ensures that perigenous subsidiary cells are balanced symmetrically around the guard cells; this effectively isolates the guard cells from the epidermal cells and may be of significance in the mechanics of opening (§ 1.3.1). In other plant groups protodermal cells are usually randomly ordered so that the stomatal meristemoid may be bordered by a variable number of protodermal cells. The symmetrical arrangement of subsidiary cells under such circumstances can only be assured by mesogenous stomatal development.

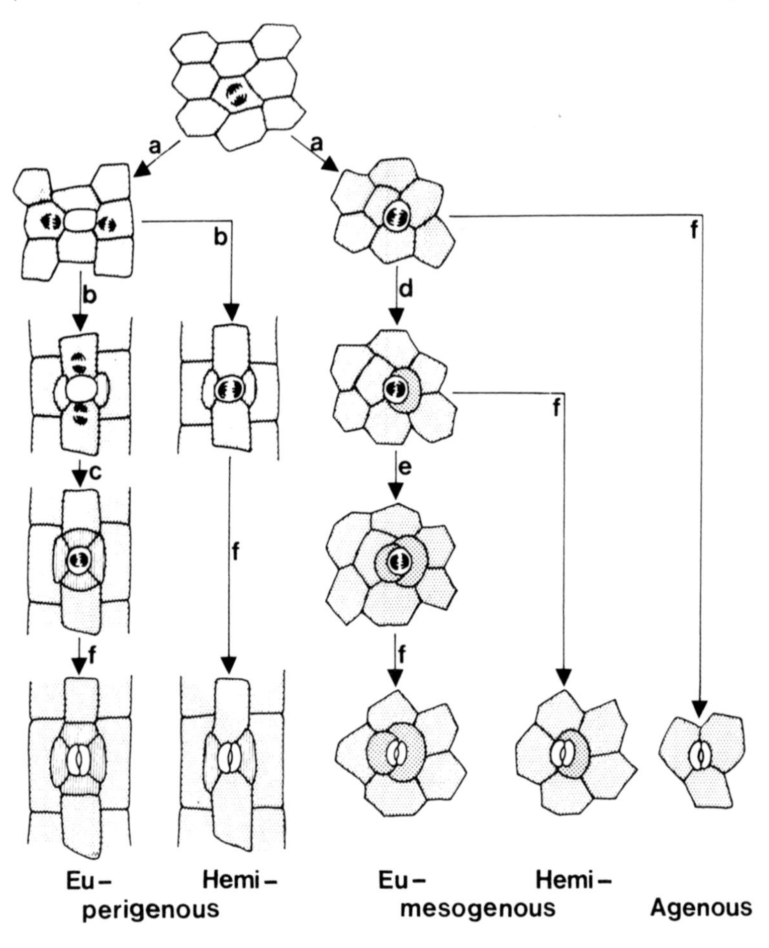

Fig. 1-2 Developmental pathways of stomatal complexes. Protodermal → epidermal/neighbouring cells are cross-hatched, stomatal meristemoids → guard cells are unshaded, perigene subsidiary cells are vertically-hatched and mesogene subsidiary cells are stippled. Illustrating development of: (a) stomatal meristemoid, (b) lateral perigene subsidiary cells, (c) polar perigene subsidiary cells, (d) mesogene subsidiary cell, (e) second mesogene subsidiary cell and (f) guard cell pairs. If the guard cells are completely surrounded and contacted by subsidiary cells, their developmental pathway is prefixed *eu-*, if they are surrounded and contacted by both subsidiary and neighbouring cells, they are prefixed *hemi-*. Very occasionally guard cells may be found which are associated with both perigenous and mesogenous subsidiary cells and their developmental pathway is referred to as *mesoperigenous*.

As guard cells develop in the epidermis, gaps or substomatal chambers appear in the mesophyll tissue immediately below the stomatal complexes. These chambers act as gaseous reservoirs which extend deeply into the mesophyll (Fig. 1-4) and thus maximize the diffusion of carbon dioxide to the photosynthetic tissues and at the same time increase the diffusion pathway of water vapour from the mesophyll to the stomatal pore and so reduce water loss from the photosynthetic tissues.

1.3 The guard cell wall and stomatal mechanics

The initial development of guard cells is identical in all plant groups with the immature guard cell pair fused together by their ventral walls. The principal changes which occur during the physical maturation of the guard cells are the differentiation of the cell walls and the development of the stomata.

At an early stage of development, microtubules aggregate in the cytoplasm adjacent to the guard cell plasmalemma. The microtubules are specifically orientated and dictate the direction in which the cellulose micellae are laid down in the cell wall. The resulting micellae radiate out around the cell walls from the centre of the guard cell pair. At the same time, certain regions of the cell walls become especially thickened. This thickening occurs chiefly along the outer and inner margins of the ventral walls of the guard cells with cell wall materials being deposited on the internal face of the walls so that they eventually impinge on the contents of the cells (Fig. 1-4). The formation of the stoma is initiated by an enzymatic breakdown of the pectinaceous middle lamella of the fused ventral walls of the guard cell pair and the ultimate separation of the pair is probably facilitated by an increase in turgor in the cells which forces the thickened regions of the two cells outwards so that a pore forms between the two.

After the formation of the stoma, further differentiation of the cell walls in graminaceous and elliptic guard cells is very different.

As elliptic guard cells continue to mature, there is a further increase in the cell wall deposits along the outer and inner margins of their ventral walls. Eventually these ridges become heavily cutinized and form thickened ledges which protect the throat of the stoma. Whilst the outer ledges are present in the great majority of species, the inner ledges may be greatly reduced or even absent in others (Fig. 1-3). Immediately after the stoma of graminaceous guard cells forms, the middle regions of the outer and inner guard cell walls become greatly thickened and rod-like to form the typical dumbell-shaped guard cells at maturity (Fig. 1-1).

1.3.1 Stomatal mechanics

The process of opening and closing the stoma is achieved by osmotic volume changes in the guard cells which results in differential expansion of the cells as dictated by guard cell structure. In elliptic guard cells, the cellulose micellae radiate away from the stoma and encircle the cells so that as the volume of the cell increases radial expansion is constrained by the micellae and the bulk of the

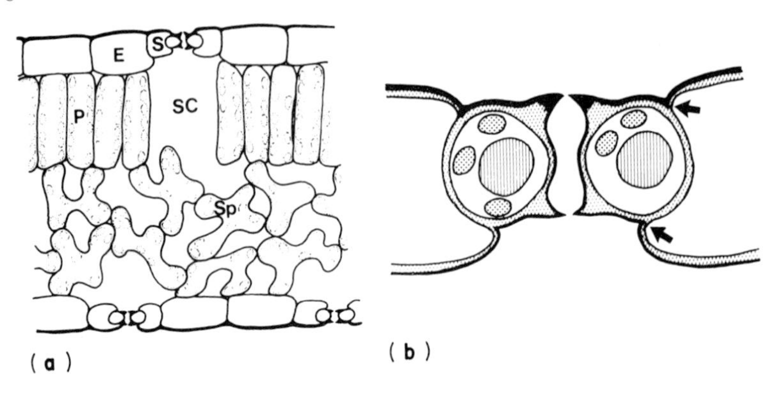

Fig. 1-3 (**a**) V.S. through a typical mesophyte leaf. E, epidermal cell; P, palisade mesophyll cell; S, subsidiary cell; Sp, spongy mesophyll cell; SC, substomatal chamber. (**b**) T.V.S. through a pair of elliptic guard cells showing outer and inner cuticularized ledges. The arrows indicate Schwendener's Hautgelenke. Cell walls, cross-hatched; nuclei, vertically-hatched; plastids, stippled. The thick margins represent cuticularized surfaces.

expansion is directed towards the poles (Fig. 1-1). The resultant linear extension is restricted in the region adjacent to the stoma by the thickened ledges with the result that the cell bends away from the stoma to produce an opening movement. The expansion of the guard cells into their surrounding cells (Fig. 1-1) is facilitated, in some species, by Schwendener's Hautgelenke (*Germ* 'skin hinges') which are especially thin areas of the latter cell walls where they attach onto the guard cells (Fig. 1-3). The Hautgelenke allow the guard cells to bulge into their adjacent cells to accommodate opening. The movements of the guard cells are not only dependant on their own osmotic status but are modified by the turgidity of their surrounding cells. The degree of stomatal opening is the result of an osmotic imbalance between the guard and their adjacent cells. Thus, if one of these adjacent cells in an open stomatal complex is punctured and loses its turgor, the guard cell on that side of the complex will bend out even further and the stomatal aperture becomes larger.

In graminaceous stomata, the central regions of each guard cell are extremely rigid whilst the bulbous polar ends are comparatively thin-walled and have radiating micellae (Fig. 1-1). As the volume of the guard cell pair increases, the polar ends balloon out and press against their opposite number. In this way the rigid central regions bounding the stoma are forced apart.

1.3.2 Plasmodesmata and ectodesmata

Plasmodesmata are microscopic cytoplasmic strands which interconnect adjacent cells and function as transport pathways. These structures occur throughout the mesophyll and epidermal tissues but are absent from mature guard and subsidiary cells, so there can be no direct passage of metabolites to them from either the mesophyll or the epidermis, and vice versa. Any passage of metabolites to and from these cells must take place indirectly *via* the aqueous phase of the cell walls (§ 4.1).

Ectodesmata are more problematic structures because they are of an extremely transient nature and can be best described as preferential transport channels through cell walls which lack any permanent structure. They have been commonly reported from the outer guard cell walls, especially in the region of their juncture with the dorsal walls. The number of ectodesmata varies with environmental factors and are most numerous in the dark and at low temperatures. Their function is uncertain but it has been suggested that they might be sites for foliar absorption, cutin deposition or peristomatal transpiration (§ 2.5). Similar structures have also been found at the juncture of the dorsal and inner guard cell walls extending from just beneath the endocuticle and up the dorsal wall to just beneath the plasmalemma of the guard cell and probably act as channels for ion transport.

1.3.3 Substomatal ion-adsorbent bodies

Discrete ion-adsorbent bodies occur beneath the poles of the guard cell pair in many ferns and the monocotyledon families Commelinaceae (spiderworts) and herbaceous Araceae (arums) (Fig. 4-4d). The bodies are of a pectinaceous nature and lie in an extracellular position between the inner guard cell walls and the endocuticle which, in the ferns, at least, is extended into an endocuticular sac. The sac itself interconnects with the endocuticle of the adjacent cells by pectin-filled folds or trabeculae. The function of the substomatal ion-adsorbent bodies is not understood although it has been established that they can absorb a wide variety of ions, including potassium, and may act as ionic reservoirs associated with stomatal movements (§ 4.1).

1.4 Guard cell organelles

Only a cursory microscopical examination of a piece of epidermal tissue stripped off a leaf is required to establish that guard cells differ at a subcellular level from other epidermal cells in the abundance of their organelles. The most obvious difference in a typical angiosperm is that whilst epidermal cells are either devoid of functional chloroplasts, or possess only a few, guard cells are rich in chloroplasts. Most typical guard cells have about ten plastids per cell although there tend to be more in shade plants and as many as fifty plus in many ferns (Fig. 1-4). Despite their conspicuousness, the photosynthetic thylakoid membrane systems of the plastids are only weakly organized into granal stacks. Another unusual feature of the guard cell plastids in some species is a network of microtubules which extends around the periphery of the organelle. This peripheral reticulum is probably involved in the transport of metabolites between the plastids and the surrounding cytoplasm; it is a typical feature of bundle sheath plastids in C_4 plants.

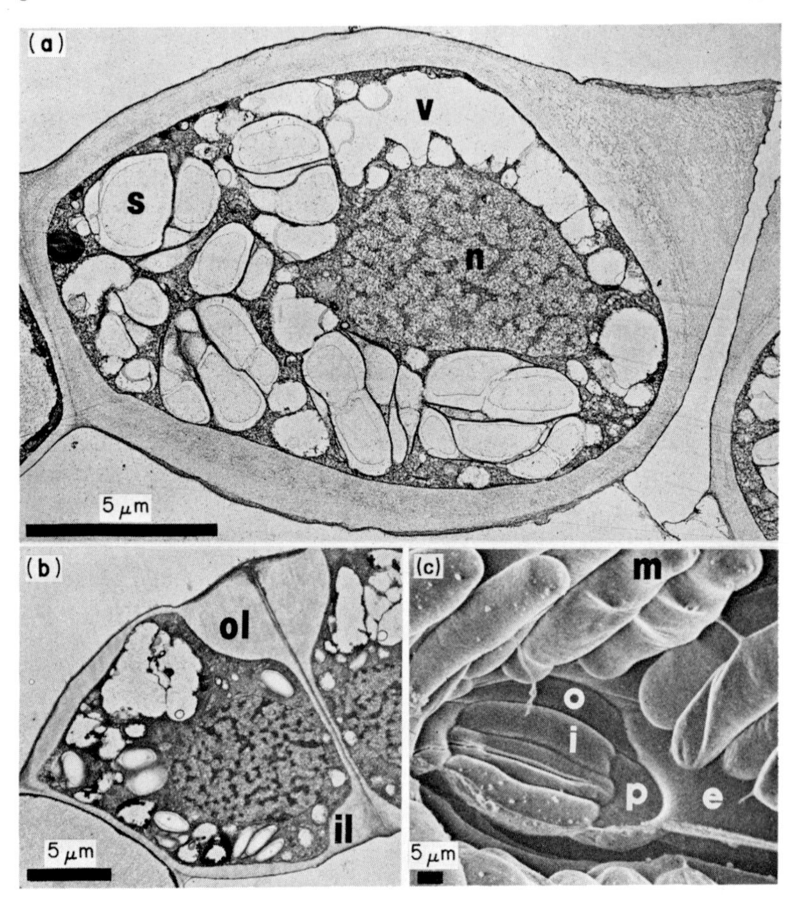

Fig. 1-4 (**a**) Transmission electron micrograph of a T.V.S. through a guard cell of *Polypodium vulgare* (common polypody fern) showing the massively-developed outer cuticularized ledge adjacent to the stoma, starch inclusion bodies (s), vacuoles (v), and nucleus (n). (**b**) Transmission electron micrograph of T.V.S. through an immature guard cell of *Polypodium vulgare*, illustrating the deposition of cell wall material during the development of the outer and inner ledges (ol and il). The guard cell pair are just beginning to separate. (**c**) Scanning electron micrograph of the stomatal complex of *Commelina communis* as viewed from within the leaf. Note how the palisade mesophyll cells (m) abut onto the epidermal cells (e) but not onto the polar (p), outer lateral (o) and inner lateral (i) subsidiary cells.

The plastids of guard cells are very rich in starch inclusion bodies (Fig. 1-4). However, if a comparison is made between the starch inclusions of open guard cells in the light and closed guard cells in the dark, it will be seen that starch accumulates in the dark and decreases in the light (§ 5.2); the reverse of what would be expected in normal photosynthetic tissue. Starch is an almost ubiquitous feature of guard cells although some *Allium* spp. (onion) lack any starch in their guard cells but their plastids are inconspicuous in any case.

As in other cells, guard cell plastids are not stationary and it has been observed that as guard cells open, the plastids become distributed around the periphery of the cells, although this migration could be attributed to displacement as guard cell vacuolar volume increases. There are also reports that the volume of guard cell plastids becomes greatly reduced during stomatal opening and it is possible that this reduction in size could be connected to changes in the volume of starch inclusion bodies as they become hydrolysed (§ 5.2).

The nuclei of guard cells are about the same size as those of other epidermal cells which, in effect, makes them relatively huge because of the reduced volume of guard cells. In fact, in graminaceous guard cells, the nucleus becomes wedged in the narrow central waist of the cell and protrudes from both ends, or may even become divided into two halves. It is reported that the nuclei of elliptic guard cells may change from an elongate form in the closed state to a round form when the stomata open, but this may reflect a change in diameter of the guard cell during stomatal movements.

Guard cells are particularly well endowed with mitochondria which are between five and ten times more numerous within guard cells on a *per* volume basis than in mesophyll tissues. Similarly, guard cells are rich in spherosomes which are membrane-bound inclusions which exhibit acid phosphatase activity. Guard cells also contrast with other epidermal cells in certain other features. For instance, the guard cells may contain oil inclusions which are often absent elsewhere in the epidermis (e.g. *Philodendron scandens*, sweetheart vine); the guard cells usually lack crystal inclusions which may be present in considerable quantities in other epidermal cells (e.g. calcium oxalate crystals in *Commelina communis*, dayflower (Fig. 4-4f); or they may lack anthocyanin pigments which pervade other epidermal cells (e.g. *Setcreasea purpurea*, purple heart).

A knowledge of the structure of guard cells is an essential requirement to our understanding of stomatal physiology. As illustrated in the following chapters, many of the basic hypotheses put forward to account for certain aspects of stomatal behaviour have been based on structural observations of guard cell organization. It is particularly important to consider guard cell complexes as metabolic islands which have no direct connections (i.e. plasmodesmata) with their adjoining tissues. Therefore, any rapid stomatal response must arise from the guard cell's own metabolic machinery unless those responses result from environmentally-induced turgor changes within the guard cell complex itself.

2 The Response of Stomata to Environmental Factors

In view of the amount of information we now have on stomatal behaviour, it is worthwhile reflecting that Francis Darwin evaluated many of the basic stomatal responses to environmental factors towards the end of the last century using the most primitive, yet functional, instrumentation. He measured stomatal movements indirectly using ingenious hygrometers made from slivers of sheep's horn or *Yucca* leaf fibres to measure relative transpiration rates. By measuring the ability of these hygrometers to 'curl' in response to changes in humidity, Darwin investigated the effects of water stress, light, darkness, carbon dioxide and temperature on stomatal behaviour. Later workers have substantiated his findings with the single exception of the effect of light quality; he found little response to blue light.

The most obvious environmental factor which affects all plants unremittingly is the alternation of night and day so that leaves are constantly exposed to a light/dark cycle. With the passage of plants from darkness to light, the basic photosynthetic machinery starts to operate and carbon dioxide is fixed in the plastids of most plants. Since stomata are the portals of gaseous diffusion in leaves, it is not surprising that the two ubiquitous factors which affect their behaviour on a daily basis are light and carbon dioxide. Since light has an indirect control over the carbon dioxide concentrations within the milieu of plant tissues *via* photosynthesis, it can often be difficult to delimit what individual effects these two environmental factors have on stomatal behaviour.

It is important to remember that a number of environmental factors can exert their own individual effects on stomatal behaviour at any one time so that the resultant stomatal aperture is an expression of the interaction of these factors.

2.1 Light

With the major exception of certain succulent plants which exhibit Crassulacean Acid Metabolism (§ 3.4), most plants open their stomata during the day and close them during the night. It is essential to remember that stomata have their own endogenous controls which express themselves in a circadian rhythm of opening and closing (§ 3.2). For this reason, it may be impossible to induce open stomata in the light to close completely by subjecting them to an artificial dark regime or to get stomata to open fully at night by providing them with a light treatment.

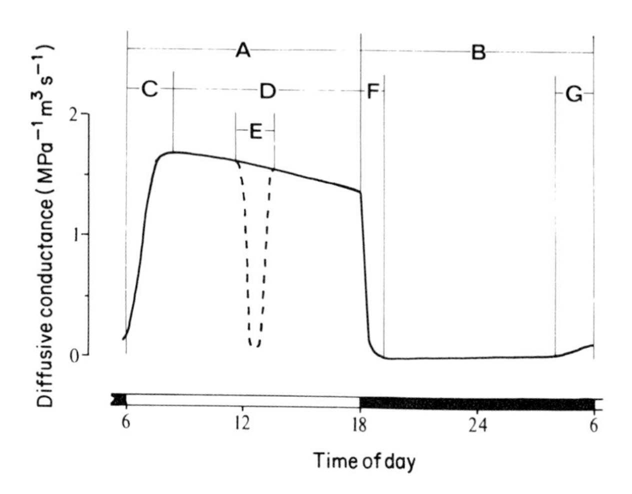

Fig. 2-1 Stomatal behaviour in *Commelina communis* over a 24 h period as recorded by a viscous flow porometer (measures leaf porosity). A, photoperiod; B, dark period; C, opening response; D, steady state opening; E, midday closure (not found in all spp.); F, closing response; and G, night opening.

The typical diurnal response of plants to sunny, cloudless conditions consists of five main elements (Fig. 2-1). During the early hours of sunlight, stomata generally open rather slowly before reaching an optimum which is maintained during the greater part of the day. This is known as steady state opening. Steady state opening tends to decay during the latter half of the photoperiod before the stomata close very rapidly at the onset of night. The stomata remain closed throughout the night but often show a weak opening movement in the hours immediately preceding dawn. This opening prior to sunrise is known as night opening (§ 3.2). Under normal conditions in temperate regions, steady state opening is not constant since periodic cloud cover may induce a temporary, or transient, decrease in stomatal aperture. Similarly in some species growing under tropical conditions, it is not unusual for the stomata to close temporarily around midday in a phenomenon known as midday closure (§ 2.3).

The initial opening behaviour of stomata in the morning usually continues for about two hours in most mesophytes until steady state opening is achieved, but it may take little more than half an hour in some plants such as *Xanthium strumarium* (cocklebur). The duration of the opening phase and the magnitude of steady state opening can be directly correlated with the prevalent light conditions and the underlying endogenous rhythm (e.g. there is evidence that the stomatal response can be conditioned by environmental factors prevailing during the previous day). At low light intensities, stomatal opening is sluggish and produces a low steady state opening, but as light intensity increases, the opening response becomes more rapid and the eventual steady state opening is greater. The speed of opening and the level of steady state opening only increases up to an optimal light intensity after which increased irradiance will neither accelerate the opening process nor result in a wider steady state opening. The amount of light required to achieve maximal opening varies greatly between species but is usually considerably less than full sunlight value.

The minimum amount of light required to induce stomatal opening also varies between species but experiments with dark-grown etiolated wheat plants (*Triticum*) (VIRGIN, 1956) suggest that only 1 – 2% of full sunlight intensity is required to induce a distinct opening response although a transpirational response was detected at an intensity as low as 10 lux (*c*. 0.01% full sunlight value). These experiments on etiolated plants are not, perhaps, a true measure of stomatal photosensitivity but it is known that the stomata of tobacco respond to light intensities of *c*. 2.5% of full sunlight.

The action spectrum for stomatal opening is essentially similar to that for photosynthesis, but increased sensitivity in the blue-light region of the spectrum indicates that guard cells are capable of light reactions which are independent of carbon dioxide concentrations and photosynthesis. MOURAVIEFF (1958) found that spectral efficiency was related to the degree of stomatal opening in leaves of *Veronica beccabunga* (brooklime) floated on water. For full stomatal opening (5 – 6μm), blue light of 464 nm was 24 times more efficient than red light of 660 nm, whereas for smaller openings (3 – 4 μm), blue light was only 4 times as efficient as red light. Similarly KUIPER (1964) was able to show that epidermal strips of *Senecio odoris* (ragwort), when exposed to identical quanta, produced only half the opening in red light compared to that in blue light (Fig. 2-2). MANSFIELD and MEIDNER (1966) have shown that stomata are able to respond to spectral intensities which were otherwise too low to produce a photosynthetic response, which infers that stomata can function below the light compensation point for photosynthesis by virtue of their blue light sensitivity. This stomatal response must be carbon

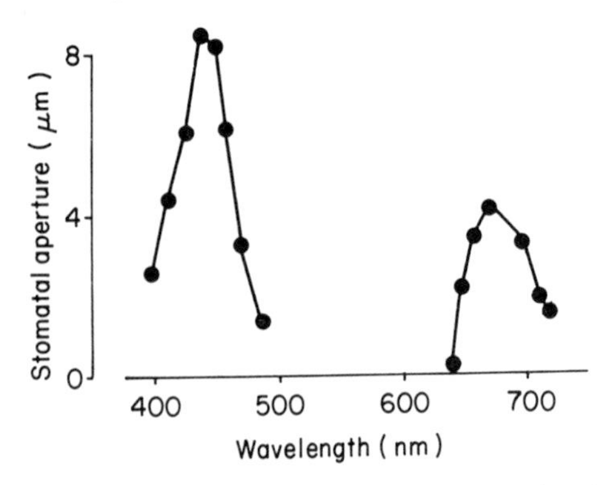

Fig. 2-2 Stomatal opening response in *Senecio odoris* to wavelengths at an irradiance of 1.14 nE cm^2 s^{-1} (after KUIPER, 1964).

dioxide-independant and cannot be due to a photosynthetic reduction of carbon dioxide levels in the intercellular space system. Interestingly, it has recently been shown that the guard cells of *Paphiopedilum* spp. (slipper orchids) lack chloroplasts but nevertheless react more positively to blue than red light.

In subsequent chapters (4 and 5) it will be shown that certain ions, such as potassium and malate, play an essential role in stomatal movements. It is pertinent, therefore, that HSIAO *et al.* (1973) found that at low quanta flux (7×10^{14} Q cm^{-2} s^{-1}), only blue and long ultra-violet light activated $^{86}Rb^+$ (used as a radioactive tracer for K^+) uptake by guard cells, whereas, at higher quanta (38×10^{14} Q cm^{-2} s^{-1}) both rubidium uptake and photosynthesis were only weakly stimulated by red light. Malate formation in guard cells is also enhanced in the blue light wavelengths. The photoreceptor for these blue light responses has yet to be identified but is believed to be a flavin pigment system which may be located in the tonoplast of the guard cell (§ 4.3).

Another interesting aspect of stomatal behaviour is that adaxial and abaxial stomata respond differently to the environment and to light in particular. Whilst the adaxial guard cells are normally exposed to direct sunlight, the abaxial guard cells only receive transmitted or reflected light. The quality of light reaching the abaxial surface of the leaf is largely filtered by the mesophyll and contains less than 10% of the blue and red light falling on the adaxial surface. If the stomata of both surfaces were to behave identically, it would follow that the adaxial stomata should open faster and wider than the abaxial ones. However, the abaxial stomata open both wider and faster than the adaxial ones; a fact that cannot be correlated to the differences in stomatal density between the two leaf surfaces. The abaxial stomata show an opening response at lower light intensities than the adaxial stomata, and the adaxial stomata start to close at higher intensities than the abaxial stomata. Experiments indicate that the differences cannot be attributed to carbon dioxide gradients within the leaf since flushing the intercellular spaces with carbon dioxide-free air does not alter the situation. There is some evidence which would support the view that there are differences between the metabolic machinery of the adaxial and abaxial guard cells since it has been found that starch hydrolysis and potassium accumulation is greater in abaxial guard cells.

2.2 Carbon dioxide

The carbon dioxide concentrations that we are concerned with here are the intracellular levels which are dependant on the metabolic processes of the cells themselves and the intercellular levels which are dependant on stomatal aperture and atmospheric carbon dioxide concentration (0.03%). Consequently, few stomata immediately respond to changes in the external ambient carbon dioxide levels, but most respond rapidly to changes in intercellular levels. Within the physiological range of carbon dioxide levels, it can be generally stated that stomata open as carbon dioxide levels decrease and close as the levels rise. Most stomata are, however, insensitive to reductions in carbon dioxide levels below 0.01% with the exception of plants such as *Zea mays* (maize) whose guard cells are sensitive to carbon dioxide concentrations approaching zero.

The fact that carbon dioxide has an effect on stomata which is independent of both light and photosynthetic activity can be best illustrated by the fact that plants whose intercellular spaces are flushed with carbon dioxide-free air fail to close their stomata completely at night. Furthermore, closed stomata in the dark will open in response to their intercellular spaces being flushed with carbon dioxide-free air.

All the evidence points to the fact that the carbon dioxide effect is not mediated by light *via* photosynthesis. This being the case, how does carbon dioxide affect the stomatal mechanism? It has been suggested that it may affect oxidative phosphorylation and the supply of ATP utilized by ion pumps and it is also thought that carbon dioxide may affect the ion fluxes through guard cell membranes and thus alter the osmotic balance (§ 5.1).

2.3 Temperature

In 1898, Darwin noted that an increase in temperature resulted in an increased stomatal opening both in the light and in the dark but that it also slowed down the rate of the closing phase. LOFTFIELD (1921) further showed that an increase in temperature led to a decrease in the time taken for the stomata to reach their steady state opening phase (Fig. 2-3). Since then these findings have been confirmed by other workers although it has also been reported that some species do not respond to temperature at all or may even show a decreased stomatal aperture with increased temperature.

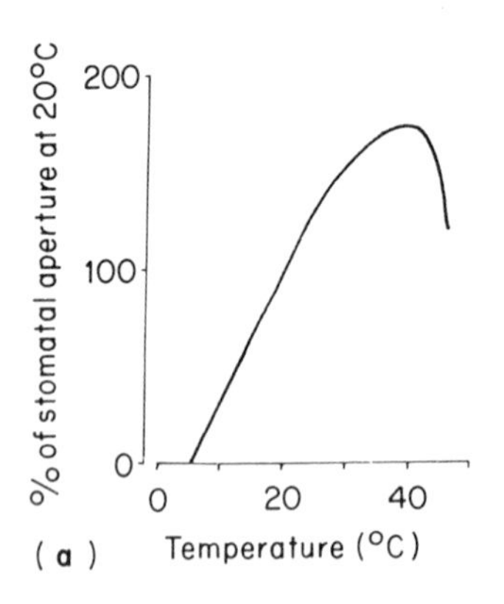

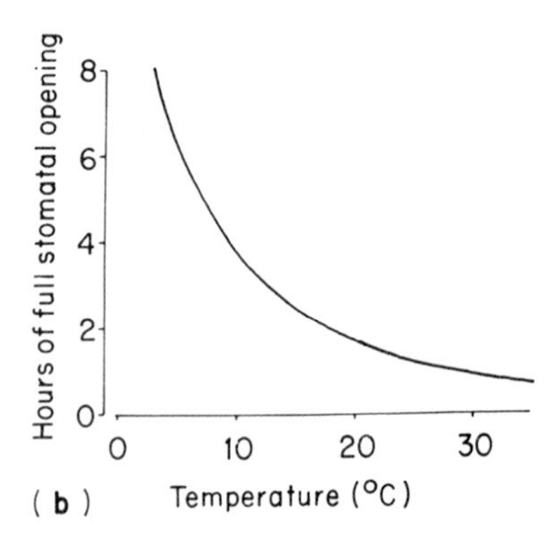

Fig. 2-3 Effect of temperature on stomatal opening. (**a**) Effect on the stomatal aperture of *Vicia faba* (broadbean) in the light at 20 klx. The degree of stomatal opening is expressed as a percentage of that at 20°C (after STALFELT, 1962). (**b**) Effect on the speed of opening in alfalfa (after LOFTFIELD, 1921).

An increase in temperature will increase the rate of enzymatically-controlled reactions so that, in the light, photosynthesis will proceed at a higher rate with a consequent depression of intercellular and intracellular carbon dioxide levels. Thus temperature can have an indirect effect on stomatal aperture *via* carbon dioxide concentrations. However, as temperature increases above the optimum for photosynthesis, carbon dioxide levels will begin to build up and this increase is the most likely explanation to account for observed stomatal closure at higher temperatures (Fig. 2-3).

A build up of carbon dioxide through a depression of photosynthetic efficiency at high temperature combined with enhanced carbon dioxide production is also believed to be the cause of midday closure in certain species. This was substantiated by MEIDNER and HEATH (1959) who were able to reverse midday closure in onion at 34°C by blowing carbon dioxide-free air through the intercellular spaces of the leaf.

It has also been found that an increase in temperature during the night hastened the onset of night opening and increased its amplitude. This suggests that temperature-induced enhancement of night opening, at least, must override the increased respiratory carbon dioxide output generated by a rise in temperature.

2.4 Water stress

Responses of stomata to water stress must be regarded as fundamental both to plant survival and efficient crop production. The guard cells act as the first line of defence against water stress by being able to regulate their aperture to prevent unnecessary transpirational losses at the same time as maintaining photosynthetic efficiency. Complete stomatal closure is usually not the answer to water stress since such stress is frequently associated with high irradiance levels and a minimal transpirational loss is advantageous since it effectively cools the plant.

Since stomatal aperture is governed by an osmotic imbalance between the guard cells and their surrounding cells, the first response of the stoma to the onset of water stress is to open slightly temporarily. This results from water being withdrawn from the epidermis into the mesophyll tissue but, since the guard cells are not in immediate contact with the mesophyll, water is withdrawn from the surrounding epidermal cells before it is withdrawn from the guard cells. As a consequence, the surrounding epidermal cells become relatively flaccid temporarily, allowing the guard cells a turgor advantage which results in stomatal opening. This opening phase is only transient and as water stress continues, water passes out of the guard cells to the mesophyll cells *via* the surrounding cells. Thus the stomata close progressively with increasing water stress. Such guard cell movements are referred to as hydropassive since they result directly from water availability rather than from the metabolic activity of the guard cells.

Similar hydropassive responses occur when a leaf is excised from a well-watered plant (Fig. 2-4). However, the first transient movement which occurs

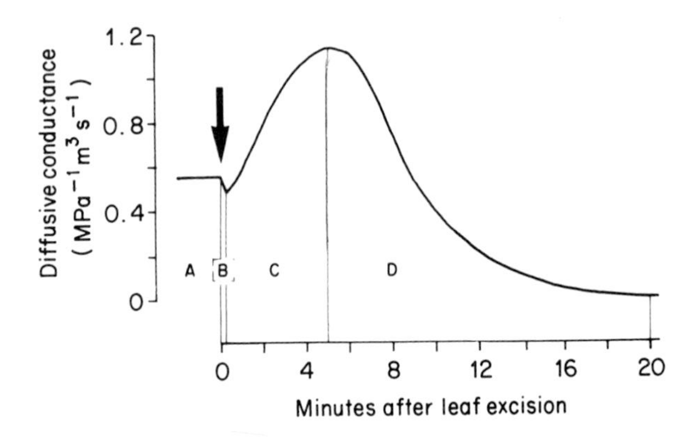

Fig. 2-4 Stomatal behaviour in *Commelina communis* following leaf excision. A, steady state opening level; B, first closing movement following leaf excision; C, opening phase; D, final closing phase. The arrow indicates the point of leaf excision.

within the first five seconds after excision and lasts for about 20 seconds is a small closing movement which arises from the tension being released in the continuous water columns of the xylem. This results in water flooding into the mesophyll and epidermis so that the cells surrounding the guard cells gain a temporary turgor advantage over the guard cells. This phase is immediately followed by an opening phase which lasts for about 100 seconds, after which the stomata start their closing phase as water is lost from the guard cells.

It has been found that starch accumulates in leaves as they wilt so that if an epidermal strip is removed from a leaf, the guard cells in the remaining tissue becomes rich in starch; a process which can be prevented if the leaf is floated on water. Similarly, GLINKA and MEIDNER (1968) found that wilted leaves of *Xanthium strumarium* floated on water show a positive correlation between the degree of water stress and the speed of the opening phase and a negative correlation between the degree of stress and the amplitude of the steady state opening. HEATH and MEIDNER (1961) have also shown that wheat leaves floated on water and at a light intensity of 9 klx have a carbon dioxide compensation point of 0.008% whilst similar leaves floated on 0.4 M mannitol have a compensation point of 0.012%. Floating on the mannitol solution also led to stomatal closure. Water stress, therefore, leads to an increased carbon dioxide sensitivity in the guard cells.

Normal stomatal opening does not occur for several days after a plant regains its normal turgor following a period of water stress. This failure of stomata to respond in a normal way occurs in spite of the carbon dioxide compensation point quickly returning to near normal following the restitution of normal turgor. Indeed sweeping the intercellular spaces of the leaf with carbon dioxide-free air will not normalize stomatal behaviour. The sluggish return to normal stomatal behaviour is clearly not a carbon dioxide-dependant phenomenon.

In 1969, WRIGHT and HIRON found that abscisic acid (ABA) was synthesized in leaves which were subjected to water stress. It was subsequently discovered that the exogenous application of ABA to leaves also brought about stomatal closure and that its effect on stomata persisted for several days. Furthermore, if the intercellular spaces of ABA-treated leaves are swept with carbon dioxide-free air, the stomata remain closed. It is believed that the sluggish normalization of stomatal behaviour following water stress is due to the endogenous synthesis of ABA which prevents potassium uptake and starch hydrolysis in the guard cells (§ 6.2).

2.5 Air humidity

When we talk about transpiration, we normally think in terms of water evaporating from the surfaces of cells within the leaf and diffusing out into the surrounding air through the stomata. However, even when stomata are completely closed, transpiration can still continue, albeit at a very diminished rate, *via* the epidermal cell walls and cuticle in cuticular transpiration. Cuticular transpiration is greatest in the region of the guard cell pair and this localized transpirational pathway is referred to as peristomatal transpiration. The most likely pathway for peristomal transpiration are the ectodesmata (§ 1.3.2). Peristomatal transpiration does not contribute a constant proportion of total transpirational loss but may vary with the numbers of ectodesmata present at any one time, the state of the stomatal aperture and the ambient relative humidity.

The importance of air humidity as a factor affecting stomata has been largely overlooked by plant physiologists although reports on its role in stomatal behaviour were first published in the last century. It is only in the last decade that serious studies have been made and we now know that the stomata of a considerable number of species can respond directly to changes in ambient humidity, whereas others appear to be unaffected. It is difficult to correlate these differences in responses to any particular feature which separates the two groups. It would seem, however, that plants whose epidermes are only loosely or sparsely connected to their underlying mesophyll tissues tend to have more responsive stomata. The cuticle and its state of development must also play some role in humidity responses.

Guard cells close in response to low air humidity when their water potential becomes less than that of the ambient air and the speed of the closing response is proportional to the water potential difference. Thus the response is most pronounced in well-watered plants exposed to dry air.

The response is a hydropassive one and as such infers that the guard cells themselves are the humidity sensors. It has been assumed over the years that the mesophyll walls are the major site of transpirational water loss but this has been questioned by MEIDNER (1975) who suggested that the inner face of the epidermis abutting onto the substomatal chamber acts as the major evaporative site. These epidermal evaporative sites are particularly important in those species which have poor hydraulic conductivity between the mesophyll

3 Endogenous Control of Stomatal Movements

3.1 Circadian rhythms in stomatal behaviour

Stomata not only respond to external factors such as light, temperature, humidity and carbon dioxide concentration, but they also show rhythmic behaviour with a repeated frequency of approximately 24 hours under constant environmental conditions. These rhythms of opening and closing of the stomatal pore appear to be controlled from within the plant and are therefore called endogenous or circadian rhythms (Latin: *circa* – about; *diem* – a day). It is hardly surprising that this periodicity evolved since the most dominant environmental change on the earth is the alternation of day with night and almost all living organisms show the same rhythmic behaviour (BRADY, 1979). The study of these rhythmic processes in living organisms is sometimes referred to as chronobiology, because they appear to reflect the operation of an internal biological timing process or clock. Chronobiology has its own specialized vocabulary, some of which is defined in Fig. 3-1.

It is generally recognized that a rhythm such as that described in Fig. 3-1 is determined by two basic parameters; its period and amplitude. The period describes the time it takes for a rhythm to complete one cycle and the amplitude describes the magnitude of a rhythm. Any point on the rhythm relative to the time axis is called the phase. This term is normally extended to describe the state of progress of a rhythm relative to solar time, so that the light-phase describes the stage of a rhythm approximating to normal day time and the dark-phase describes the stage of a rhythm approximating to night time. Other descriptive terms are used to differentiate between a free-running and an entrained rhythm. Under constant environmental conditions a rhythm becomes free-running, because it is released from the restraining influence of a repeated environmental change, such as diurnal changes in light intensity or temperature. When the conditions fluctuate, the rhythm becomes entrained, because it is induced to mimic these changing conditions. The environmental factors which initiate entrainment are called 'zietgeber' (Germ: *zeit* – time; *geber* – giver), and any alteration in their timing results in a re-timing or shift in the phase of a rhythm. Such phase-shifting is an important characteristic of circadian rhythms (§ 3.2).

It was pioneering studies of Francis DARWIN (1898) and Francis LLOYD (1908) which led to the first proposal that stomatal aperture changes in a rhythmic manner. Darwin's proposal originated from his observations that open stomata closed less rapidly when exposed to darkness in the morning than the afternoon. Conversely, closed stomata opened more rapidly in the morning

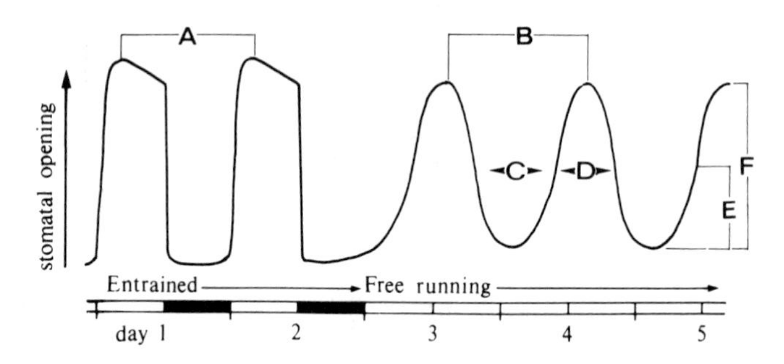

Fig. 3-1 A diagram representing an idealized circadian rhythm in stomatal movements, along with the terms used to describe various parameters of the rhythm. A, entrained or diurnal period; B, free-running period; C, dark-phase; D, light-phase; E, amplitude; and F, range of oscillation.

than in the afternoon. These early studies also revealed that stomata can open during extended periods of darkness, although the magnitude of opening was often small, and in some species repeated opening and closing movements were observed during prolonged periods of darkness.

Many of these early studies were limited by the fact that continuous records of stomatal aperture could not be obtained and therefore they relied on intermittent direct microscopic observation to ascertain whether the stomata were open or closed. The limitations of this technique in terms of both accuracy and time are fairly obvious. Later workers had the advantage of using automated viscous flow porometers, which are instruments which continuously measure the resistance to a flow of air offered by a collection of stomatal pores (MEIDNER and MANSFIELD, 1968). Viscous flow porometers measure the rate at which air can pass through a leaf when a pressure difference is exerted across the leaf. Data are usually expressed in absolute units of resistance exerted by all the stomata within a sealed porometer cup attached to the leaf and by the associated intercellular spaces of the mesophyll tissue. Alternatively, they can be presented in a semi-quantitative manner using an arbitrary scale of porometer units. This is the method used in the figures presented in this chapter; high recorder readings indicate stomatal opening and low readings stomatal closure.

3.2 Rhythms in continuous light and darkness

Early reports on the rhythmic behaviour of stomata did not distinguish between those changes that were under the direct control of environmental factors (exogenous control) and those regulated from within the plant (endogenous control). Under natural conditions there are distinct diurnal variations in light intensity, temperature and water vapour deficit. Because stomata are sensitive to small changes in all of these parameters and since many early investigations were carried out under only partially-controlled

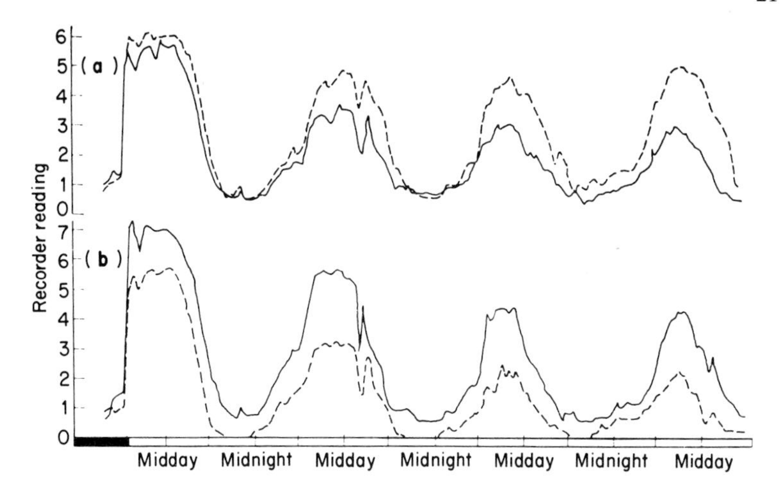

Fig. 3-2 Changes in stomatal aperture in continuous light (1500 lx) in *Tradescantia* × *andersoniana*. (**a**) and (**b**) represent continuous recordings from two leaves from two different plants (redrawn from MARTIN and MEIDNER, 1971).

environmental conditions, conclusions that these rhythmic movements were endogenous may be erroneous. Three diagnostic criteria must be satisfied before a rhythm can be said to be truly endogenous and circadian:

1) The rhythm should persist under constant environmental conditions.
2) The period should not match cyclic variations in the environment; it should be approximately 24 hours in length.
3) It should be possible to invert or reset the phase of the rhythm (phase-shift) by suitable treatments.

By placing plants in continuous light it is possible using an automated viscous flow porometer to demonstrate that stomatal rhythms persist under constant conditions and that their period is approximately 24 hours (Fig. 3-2). In these experiments and in many others described in the literature it has not yet proved possible to control all components within the environment. In particular, it has not been possible to control the ambient carbon dioxide concentration, an important factor regulating stomatal movements (§ 2.2). However, the fact that the period is not exactly 24 hours, indicates that carbon dioxide concentration and other uncontrolled elements within the enviroment were not exerting an entraining influence on the stomatal rhythm.

Possibly the most important criterion to establish the endogenous nature of a rhythm is to demonstrate its ability to show phase-shift. This can be achieved by interrupting a free-running rhythm in light with a short dark treatment (a zeitgeber) during the light-phase of the rhythm (Fig. 3-3). This causes an inversion of the rhythm, so that the post-treatment peaks of the stomatal rhythm occur much later in time. Dark treatments given during the dark-phase of the rhythm do not substantially alter the phase of the first few cycles of the

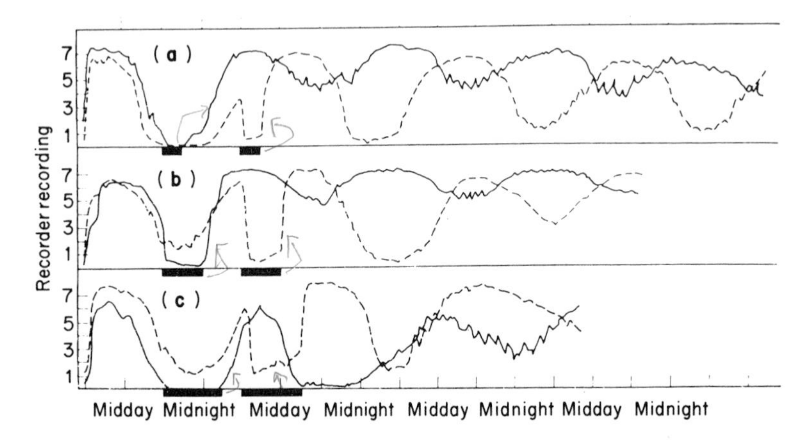

Fig. 3-3 Changes in stomatal aperture in continuous light (5000 lx) in *Tradescantia* × *andersoniana* (trinity flower) before and after short dark treatments (represented by black rectangles on the time axis) applied during different phases of the circadian rhythm. (**a**) Three hour dark treatments were applied during the dark and light-phases of the rhythm. (**b**) Six hour dark treatments were applied during the dark and light-phases. (**c**) Nine hour dark treatments were applied during the dark and light-phases respectively (redrawn from MARTIN and MEIDNER, 1971).

free-running rhythm, but in successive cycles the peaks of stomatal opening occur slightly earlier than those observed during the pretreatment time interval (Fig. 3-3).

To date the only treatment known to cause phase-shift of stomatal rhythms in continuous light are changes from light to darkness, yet in other examples of circadian rhythms within the plant kingdom, many other environmental changes can induce phase-shifts, including changes in temperature (short-term reductions in temperature mimic short dark treatments), water stress, anaerobic conditions and changes in the spectral quality of light.

In continuous darkness, a single opening cycle often occurs and this is believed to reflect the first cycle of a ciradian rhythm in darkness. This period of opening in darkness is often referred to as 'night-opening' and it occurs generally several hours after terminating the normal period of light. For example, when plants of *Tradescantia* × *andersoniana* are exposed to continuous darkness following a 12 hour photoperiod, the stomata begin to open 9 hours 14 minutes later (Fig. 3-4a). Although there was no evidence for a second cycle of opening in these experiments, it is possible to induce another cycle of night-opening following an additional 12 hour photoperiod (Fig. 3-4b). It is arguable whether these single opening cycles constitute a true rhythm, since they are not self-sustaining, such as those in continuous light. Some chronobiologists differentiate between self-sustaining or active rhythms which are capable of maintaining an oscillation and passive rhythms which only oscillate with a periodic change in the environment and 'damp' out in the

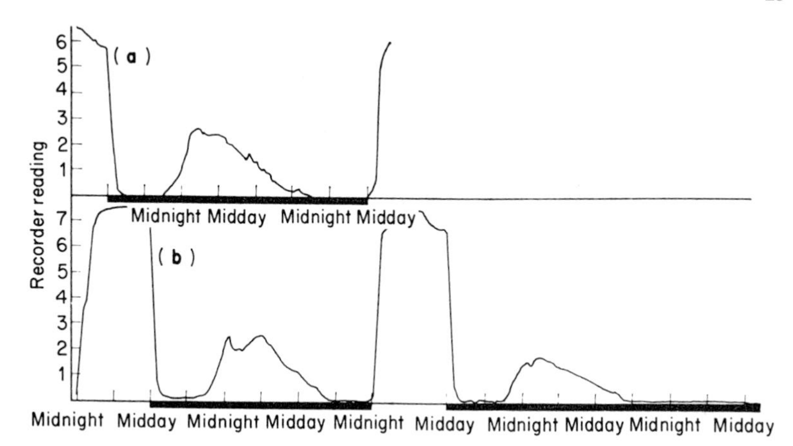

Fig. 3-4 Changes in stomatal aperture in *Tradescantia* × *andersoniana* in continuous darkness following a 12 h photoperiod. (**a**) Stomatal behaviour following a 12 h photoperiod (6 a.m. – 6 p.m.). (**b**) Stomatal behaviour following a 12 h photoperiod (12 midnight – 12 noon), showing repeated cycles of night-opening (redrawn from MARTIN and MEIDNER, 1971).

absence of an energy supply from an external source. Night-opening of stomata may reflect this distinction, since it is not unusual for some rhythms in continuous darkness to reduce their amplitude or disappear, possibly because of the depletion of some vital metabolite.

In some species it has been found that at least two cycles of night-opening occur. The Swedish stomatal physiologist, Stalfelt's painstaking studies on the common broad bean (*Vicia faba*), have revealed the existence of two successive cycles of stomatal opening in darkness. He was able to show by direct microscopic observation that the overall width of the guard cell pair changed simultaneously with the width of the pores. He also observed that the 'osmotic surplus', which is the difference between the osmotic values at incipient plasmolysis between the guard cells and epidermal cells, also exhibited a rhythm in darkness, which is synchronous with the rhythm in stomatal aperture. Since the fluctuations in the osmotic values of both guard cells and epidermal cells were often parallel, we can assume that epidermal turgor had little effect on the opening of the guard cells during these extended periods of darkness; i.e. the guard cells gained a turgor advantage over the surrounding epidermal cells.

Another feature of night-opening which is evidence of circadian behaviour is the occurrence of phase-shift. A detailed investigation of the factors which lead to phase-shift of night-opening in *Xanthium strumarium* was carried out by MANSFIELD and HEATH (1963). They found that by reducing a 16 h night with low intensity illumination they could delay the initiation of night opening and there was a positive correlation between the time that these light treatments terminated and the time that night opening began. In subsequent studies they

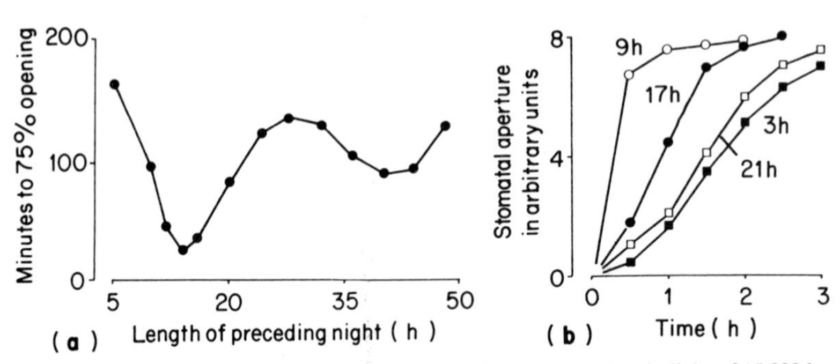

Fig. 3-5 (**a**) Opening ability of stomata in *Xanthium strumarium* in light of 15 000 lx, after different lengths of night. (**b**) rates of stomatal opening response to light of 20 000 lx, after different night lengths; these are given in hours adjacent to each response curve (redrawn from MANSFIELD and HEATH, 1963).

also found that the magnitude of phase-shift was increased when the light intensity of these pre-treatments was increased from 10 to 160 lux and that red light was more effective than blue light. They were unable to demonstrate a second cycle of night opening under conditions of prolonged darkness in *Xanthium strumarium*, although they were able to show a repeated rhythm in opening ability by measuring the rate of opening of stomata in light after exposing the plants to different lengths of night (Fig. 3-5) and this appeared to be a much more sensitve indicator of underlying rhythmic behaviour.

3.3 The significance of circadian rhythms under natural conditions

What then is the significance of these precisely-timed events leading to stomatal opening and closing? At present we are unable to make definitive conclusions, although they must play some role in synchronizing the behaviour of the numerous stomata that exist on the leaf surface. If these movements of stomata are an expression of an endogenous rhythm, they should also exhibit a periodically changing sensitivity to light and darkness. One significant observation in this context is the rapidity of stomatal opening when they are in the early stages of night opening (Fig. 3-5). Stomata in such a condition appear to be 'anticipating' dawn and are capable of opening rapidly to allow maximum carbon dioxide fixation. They also take advantage of low transpiration rates arising as a consequence of a morning atmosphere with a relatively high humidity. Even in the absence of any visible night-opening, stomata still retain this ability to open rapidly, whereas if dawn occurs at the wrong phase of the rhythm then stomatal opening is sluggish and maximum opening may not be achieved for many hours. Such desynchronization could have serious consequences both for the efficiency of photosynthesis and for the conservation of internal water levels.

The ability of stomata to close also appears to be determined by the phase of an underlying rhythm; darkness falling during the correct phase will cause closure of the pore within a short interval of time, allowing the plant an immediate opportunity to replenish its water content *via* root absorption, without the conflicting demands of transpiration. Conversely, any fluctuation in light intensity (as a result of increasing cloud cover) occurring at the incorrect phase would prevent complete closure of the stomata and ensure that photosynthetic carbon dioxide fixation could continue, albeit at a reduced level.

3.4 The stomatal behaviour of succulents

Night-opening of stomata is by no means unique to typical mesophytes, because in many species of succulents wide stomatal opening occurs at night, followed by closure during the day. This unusual behaviour is the basis of a survival strategy in those succulents inhabiting arid regions of the world, because they are capable of fixing enormous quantities of carbon dioxide into organic acids whilst the stomata are open at night, and during the day the stomata are closed to prevent water loss. This distinctive metabolism of carbon dioxide is often referred to as Crassulacean Acid Metabolism or CAM, since it was first discovered in members of the family Crassulaceae.

A more detailed analysis of this diurnal stomata behaviour indicates that it may be similar to that exhibited by mesophytes (Fig. 3-6). In mesophytes, stomata open partially in darkness in advance of dawn and also show partial closure towards the end of the day, as a consequence of an underlying rhythm. The pattern of behaviour in these two diverse groups of plant is therefore basically similar, only differing in the magnitude of stomatal opening and closing. Consequently, it has been suggested that in succulents the degree of opening at night and the degree of closure during the day is merely a more dominant development of these endogenous features to ensure carbon dioxide fixation at night and water conservation during the day.

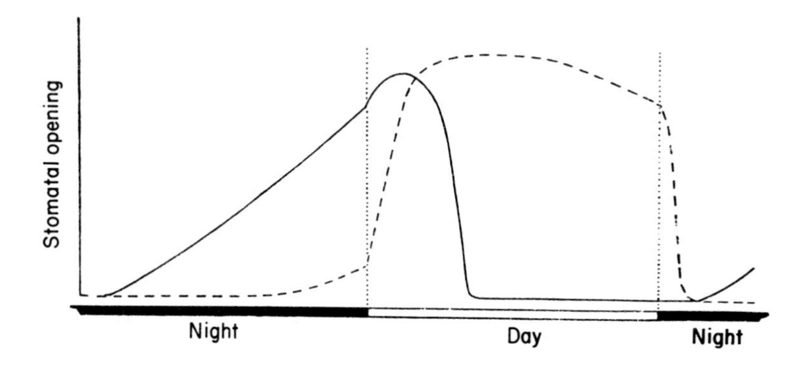

Fig. 3-6 A diagram representing the daily changes in stomatal aperture in a succulent (continuous line), and a mesophyte (broken line) (redrawn from MEIDNER and MANSFIELD, 1965).

3.5 Circadian rhythms and diurnal metabolic rhythms in guard cells

Stomatal rhythms may be manifestations of metabolic rhythms occurring within the guard cells, although the possibility of metabolic control originating from elsewhere within the leaf should not be ignored. In fact night opening of stomata in succulents is believed to be caused by low carbon dioxide concentrations in the substomatal intercellular spaces, resulting from dark carbon dioxide fixation by the enzyme phosphoenol pyruvate carboxylase in the mesophyll. Until rhythms of stomatal opening and closing have been demonstrated in isolated epidermal tissue or better still in isolated guard cells or guard cell protoplasts, we should refrain from making too many generalizations. As will be discussed later, many of the current mechanisms to explain stomatal movements rely on the fact that stomata open in light and close in darkness. That this is an oversimplification is obvious from the preceding account of stomatal rhythms. Indeed a mechanism to explain night-opening of stomata is fundamental to the study of stomatal physiology, since it cannot be explained by any of the classical theories, all of which attribute opening to changes occurring within the guard cells and surrounding cells in response to illumination.

To date only two hypotheses have been proposed to explain the mechanism of night-opening of stomata in mesophytes: the starch-sugar hypothesis of SCARTH, WHYTE and BROWN (1933) and the dark fixation hypothesis, originally proposed by HEATH (1950) and later modified by MANSFIELD and HEATH (1963).

Scarth and co-workers observed that when leaves were immersed in water or oil, night-opening occurred much earlier and increased in amplitude. From this simple observation, coupled with an observable rise of pH of the guard cell contents, they proposed that the primary cause of night-opening was the lowering of oxygen concentration within the leaf tissue (arising naturally as a result of stomatal closure or experimentally as a result of immersion in oil or water). They suggested that the reduced oxygen tension in the leaf would eventually reduce respiratory carbon dioxide evolution and cause a rise in pH of the guard cell contents. The elevated pH change could then induce the enzymatic hyrolysis of starch to sugar leading to a decreased osmotic potential within the guard cells and stomatal opening (§ 5.2). This hypothesis and in particular its reliance on the development of low oxygen levels in continuous darkness requires experimental verification, because in a natural state, once the stomata have opened the oxygen deficit is likely to become dissipated and the stomata might be expected to close immediately, a situation not borne out by experimental observation (Fig. 3-4).

The second hypothesis arose as a result of the discovery that stomata are extremely sensitive to small changes in carbon dioxide concentration and it was suggested by HEATH (1950) that a dark carbon dioxide fixation process leading to the formation of organic acids might regulate guard cell pH and hence stomatal aperture. Later, MANSFIELD and HEATH (1963) suggested that rhythmically operated CO_2 -acceptor mechanism in the guard cells might explain both night opening and the rhythmic opening ability demonstrated in *Xanthium strumarium*. As will be discussed later, there is now convincing evidence that the enzyme phosphoenol pyruvate carboxylase occurs in the guard cells. This enzyme catalyses the fixation of CO_2 into oxaloacetate, which is then rapidly reduced to malate, which eventually accumulates in the guard cells (§ 5.1). To be directly implicated in the control of rhythmic behaviour of stomata this carboxylation system should show rhythmic activity. Although there is no definitive evidence for such rhythmic activity, malate levels in the epidermis do show diurnal changes which correlate very closely with diurnal changes in stomatal aperture. Furthermore, if malate is derived from starch (§ 5.2) this could explain the well established correlations between guard cell starch content and diurnal changes in stomatal aperture.

3.6 Other types of cyclic variations in stomatal aperture

Cyclic oscillations in stomatal aperture, transpiration and photosynthetic rate which have periods of 20–100 minutes have been observed in many species (BARRS, 1971). They are usually most easily observed in constant environmental conditions and therefore like circadian rhythms appear to be autonomous. The magnitude of these cyclic changes in aperture is generally small, although depending on conditions large fluctuations may be observed. They are usually initiated by a disturbance or change in the environment, such as a rapid change from light to dark conditions or a lowering of atmospheric humidity, or by manipulation of the carbon dioxide concentration. In fact a wide array of factors can initiate cycling. There is also evidence that the stomata on one surface of a leaf can oscillate out of phase with those on the opposite surface.

Little is known about the mechanisms underlying these oscillations, although BARRS (1971) discusses the view that there are two oscillations. The first have a much shorter period (2.5–4.5 minutes in maize) and appear to be controlled via the carbon dioxide concentration within the leaf, whereas the second show a much larger period (15–39 minutes in maize) and seem to be controlled by the water relations of the plant.

One possibility is that the oscillations are evidence of negative feedback in the stomatal mechanism. Oscillations often occur in manmade control systems that employ negative feedback, because delays in the response of different parts of the system cause the control loop to overshoot. An example of this type of control is used in a thermostatically-regulated room heater. The heater is switched on when the room temperature falls below the thermostat setting, and switched off if the temperature rises above it. However, neither the heater nor the thermostat act instantaneously. Consequently, the temperature may overshoot the thermostat setting because the heater requires some time to cool down after it is switched off. Similarly, the heater requires some time to warm up when it is switched on, and the temperature may undershoot the thermostat setting.

In the same way, there may be delays in the responses of stomata to, for example, changes in carbon dioxide level within the leaf, or there may be a lag between the change in stomatal aperture and its effect on the internal environment of the leaf. Such delays would tend to make the stomatal control mechanism overshoot and oscillations would result. However, there is substantial evidence that stomatal movements cannot be explained simply in terms of negative-feedback loops. Such loops would operate to maintain a constant internal environment within the leaf regardless of changes in the surrounding air, but recent work has shown that direct responses of stomata to *external* stimuli such as light and humidity enable the plant to optimize its water use efficiency. These direct responses introduce 'feed forward' loops into the control mechanism. This type of control may be unfamiliar, but is analagous to control of the room heater described earlier by means of a themostat *outside* the room. In this way, potential changes in room temperature can, to some extent, be 'anticipated' by monitoring the air temperature outside the building. When the outside temperature falls, the heater can be switched on *before* the room temperature falls. The analogy should not be taken too far, but by similar means the plant is able to adjust its stomata in such a way that it optimizes the uptake of carbon dioxide with respect to water loss.

4 The Role of Ion Fluxes in Stomatal Movements

Although there is evidence that stomata can respond directly to physical factors in the environment, such as changes in humidity, most of their responses act through changes in their osmotic potential, which cause the guard cells to take up water and as a result of an increase in turgor, they expand (§ 1.3.3). In some species the final aperture achieved under a specific environmental condition can also be moderated by osmotic changes in the surrounding cell. In general, the osmotic potential in guard cells decrease by values of between $^{-}0.2$ to $^{-}1.0$ MPa, during stomatal opening.

4.1 The role of potassium in stomatal movements

For well over 100 years the mechanism causing the guard cell osmotic potential to decrease has been a subject of intense speculation and debate and it is only recently that aspects of the underlying mechanism have been resolved. For most of this century research focused on the starch-sugar hypothesis (§ 5.2). A new chapter in the search for an explanation of the stomatal mechanism was heralded by the independent discoveries of FUJINO (1967) and FISCHER (1968), who found that during stomatal opening guard cells accumulate large amounts of potassium ions (K^+), which they suggested could lower the osmotic potential. Surprisingly, this was not a new discovery, because the presence of K^+ in guard cells had been detected as long ago as 1905 and even some 40 years later a Japanese physiologist, Imamura had demonstrated that K^+ levels could be correlated with stomatal aperture. Although these studies were not unfamiliar to western scientists, they linked K^+ with the starch-sugar hypothesis and suggested that catalytic amounts of it were necessary for the hydrolytic activity of the enzymes involved in starch breakdown. It was FUJINO (1967) who first suggested that K^+ uptake could lower the osmotic potential of guard cells and lead to stomatal opening. He demonstrated that when the leaf epidermis of the dayflower (*Commelina communis*) was floated on solutions of KCl, its stomata opened in the light and using histochemical methods he found they accumulated K^+ in large amounts (Fig. 4-4a and b). Although these early studies strongly implicated K^+ in the regulation of guard cell turgor, they were limited by the fact that estimates of the amount of K^+ accumulating in guard cells could not be obtained by histochemical methods (§ 7.2). Subsequent research, using the uptake of radioactive rubidium chloride as a radioactive tracer for K^+, has shown that the concentration of K^+ within the guard cells increases to approximately 300 mol

m^{-3}, causing an estimated change of −1.2 MPa in the osmotic potential, assuming that K^+ is taken up as the chloride salt.

Many of these studies made use of epidermal tissue, removed from the leaves and floated in buffered solutions containing potassium chloride (Chapter 7); these experimental systems have the advantage of allowing both the chemical and physical environment of the tissue to be manipulated precisely. Stomata in these *in vitro* systems appear to show typical responses to light, darkness and carbon dioxide concentration, although the concentration of KCl in the incubating medium, required for opening, depends upon the species used. For maximal opening in *Commelina communis*, the concentration is always higher (100 – 200 mol m^{-3}) than that for *Vicia faba* (10 mol m^{-3}), which may be due in part to structural differences between the guard cells of these two species and to differences in the ionic composition of the incubating medium. For example, stomatal opening in *Vicia faba* seems to require the presence of small amounts of calcium, whereas in *Commelina communis* it is inhibited by calcium. The sensitivity of the stomata to light and carbon dioxide concentration is also affected by the concentration of KCl. In *Commelina*, recent studies have shown that an optimal concentration of about 50 mol m^{-3} is necessary, which suggests that at lower concentration, the ability of stomata to open may be limited by the supply of K^+ and at higher concentrations their inability to close may be caused by a reduction in the efflux of K^+ from the guard cells. One obvious effect of changing the concentration of KCl is to alter the level of Cl^- in the medium, which can have profound effects on the metabolism of guard cells (§ 5.1). *In vitro* studies with epidermal tissue have also provided evidence for a specific role for K^+ in stomatal opening; other monovalent ions such as Na^+, Li^+ and Cs^+, are much less effective, only supporting similar stomatal apertures at much higher concentrations (Fig. 4-1). No specificity has been found for an

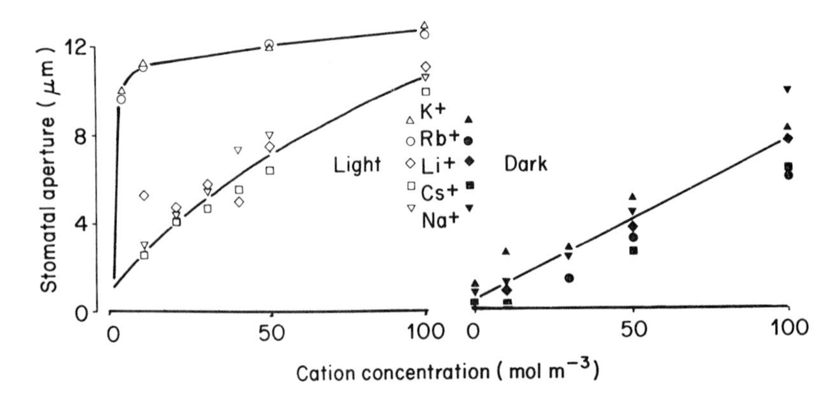

Fig. 4-1 Stomatal opening responses of *Vicia faba* epidermal tissue, incubated for 3 h on buffered media containing different concentrations of monovalent cations, under carbon dioxide-free conditions, in either light or dark conditions (redrawn from HUMBLE and HSIAO, 1969).

accompanying anion in the incubating medium, since stomatal opening is similar on solutions of KCl, KBr or KNO_3 (K_2SO_4 is slightly less effective at higher concentrations).

The use of more direct and technically more sophisticated techniques has established that K^+ is the principal ion moving into the guard cells in light. Several studies have made use of scanning electron microscopy coupled with X-ray microprobe analysis. In this technique the electron beam of the microscope causes X-rays to be generated from the elements contained within the guard cells and these X-rays can be characterized and measured by their energy level or wavelength, using crystal spectrometers (Fig. 4-4e). Estimates of guard cell K^+ concentration, based on this method range from 500 – 900 mol m^{-3} and although these values often reflect species differences, they are on the whole larger than those estimates based on the uptake of radioactive rubidium ions. Such differences probably reflect an inability to measure accurately the volumes of guard cells. This problem can be overcome by measuring the K^+ concentration directly by inserting K^+ -sensitive glass microelectrodes, with a tip diameter of *ca* 1 μm, into the guard cells. Using such sensitive experimental systems it has been established that large concentration gradients of K^+ exist across the stomatal complex of *Commelina communis*, decreasing in magnitude outwards from the guard cells in light and increasing in magnitude towards the subsidiary and epidermal cells in darkness (Fig. 4-2). These studies reveal that K^+ can accumulate against a concentration gradient, which implies that active transport of K^+ occurs during stomatal opening (§ 4.3).

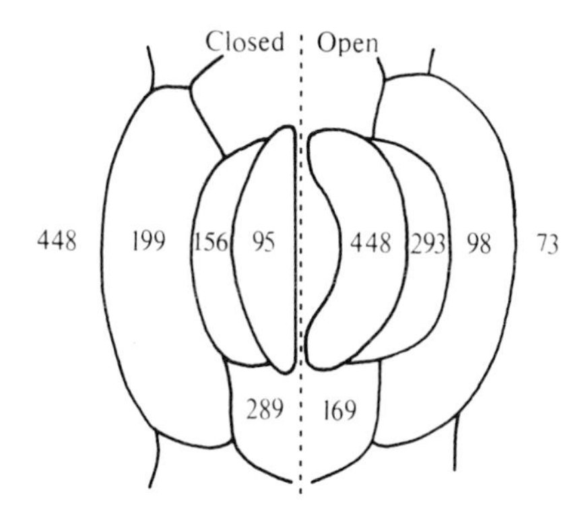

Fig. 4-2 Potassium concentrations (mol m^{-3}) in the cells of the stomatal complex of *Commelina communis*, with the stoma either closed or open (redrawn from PENNY and BOWLING, 1974).

Direct chemical analysis of the guard cell contents has been made possible by the development of techniques which can isolate the guard cells from their surrounding epidermal cells, the presence of which can constitute a major source of contamination. Partial isolation can be achieved either by rolling a plastic rod over the detached epidermis, to mechanically break the epidermal cells, or by floating epidermal tissue on buffers at pH 4.5, or by exposing the tissue to short bursts of ultrasonic irradiation. These techniques destroy all the epidermal and subsidiary cells, whilst leaving the guard cells structurally intact. Alternatively, microsurgical techniques can be used to separate *single* guard cell pairs from the epidermis; this technique coupled with sensitive microanalytical procedures has allowed analysis of K^+ levels to be made within guard cell pairs with an estimated volume of only 10^{-12} litres. Many new developments are taking place using isolated guard cell protoplasts, which have been separated from their associated walls using cellulytic enzymes (§ 7.4 and Fig. 4-4 e and f). It has been clearly demonstrated that the volume of these protoplasts increases in response to light and in the presence of K^+, in a manner analagous to the osmotic volume changes taking place in intact guard cells. Protoplasts have additional advantages because their response times to environmental factors are much shorter than those of intact stomata and volume changes can be measured more accurately than stomatal pore dimensions.

Transport of K^+ between the guard cells and their surrounding cells in the epidermis must take place through the apoplast because plasmodesmata have not been found connecting mature guard cells with their adjacent cells. However, it has not yet been established whether the solution in the apoplast supplies all the K^+ required by the guard cells, or whether additional or alternative supplies could be available from ion reservoirs within the epidermal tissue. Some species (e.g. maize) seem to possess subsidiary cells which act as ion reservoirs and in other species specific epidermal cells appear to contain more K^+ than others and these may function as storage reservoirs. The guard cells of some ferns and some members of the Commelinaceae and Araceae also have novel morphological structures associated with their walls, which could serve as ion reservoirs (§ 1.3.3; Fig. 4-4d).

Currently, K^+ has been found to accumulate in guard cells of open stomata in more than 50 species, which include mosses, ferns, and many gymnosperms and angiosperms. The only exceptions are certain halophytes, which because they inhabit saline environments, appear to utilize sodium ions, although limited evidence suggests that under non-saline conditions they may revert to K^+ as a guard cell osmoticum.

4.2 The role of inorganic anions

One possible consequence of the massive accumulation of K^+ in the guard cells during stomatal opening would be the development of a large electrical charge. If this number of positive charges were present on the surface of a body the size of a guard cell, the potential developed would be around 10^4V. The existence of such potentials is highly unlikely and therefore a mechanism must be available to balance this charge and maintain electroneutrality. There are two basic mechanisms by which electroneutrality might be achieved: (*i*) by the simultaneous transport of negatively charged anions along with K^+ into the guard cells or (*ii*) by the simultaneous transport of osmotically inactive cations out of the guard cells in exchange for K^+.

If the import of an anion maintains electroneutrality, a specific requirement for an anion species might be anticipated. However, with the exception of onion guard cells (§ 5.1), the majority of species appear to have no specific anion requirement for stomatal opening. In onion guard cells there appears to be an absolute requirement for Cl^-, whereas in other species only a small proportion (5 – 20%) of the K^+ uptake is balanced by Cl^-. Such discrepancies suggest that an additional mechanism must maintain electroneutrality. In fact there is reason to believe that stomatal opening can take place without an inorganic anion. For example, stomata open in epidermal tissue of *Vicia faba* incubated on media containing non-absorbable anions (e.g. potassium iminodiacetate – the anion, iminodiacetate, is incapable of penetrating guard cell membranes), and in this situation electroneutrality appeared to be maintained by an exchange of K^+ for H^+ (protons), because the incubating medium acidified during stomatal opening (Fig. 4-3). Protons are released

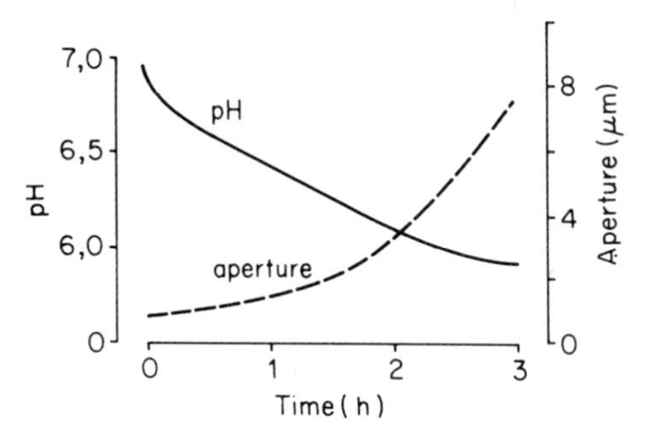

Fig. 4-3 Stomatal movements in epidermal tissue of *Vicia faba*, incubated on 5 mol m^{-3} potassium iminodiacetate and 0.1 mol m^{-3} calcium iminodiacetate in light and carbon dioxide-free conditions. Note the associated changes in the pH of the medium containing the tissue, which is believed to indicate proton extrusion (redrawn from RASCHKE and HUMBLE, 1973).

during the synthesis of organic acids within the guard cells and these could be the source of protons used in this exchange process (§ 5.1). More recent studies using sensitive pH microelectrodes inserted into guard cells also support the idea of K^+/H^+ exchange, since during stomatal opening the pH of the guard cells rises.

4.3 The mechanism driving ion transport

The evidence depicted in Fig. 4-2 clearly indicates that large concentration gradients of K^+ exist across the stomatal complex during stomatal opening and closing. Therefore K^+ transport into and out of the guard cells appears to be an active process, which implies that energy is utilized in moving ions against a concentration gradient. Both the source and the nature of the energy required for K^+ transport between the cells of the stomatal complex has been a subject of major speculation and debate, although it is generally assumed that energy in the form of adenosine triphosphate (ATP) is involved. From a theoretical standpoint the energy for active transport of solutes may be provided by either the hydrolysis of ATP or by electron transport in association with certain redox reactions. In guard cells, which contain both mitochondria and chloroplasts, energy could be supplied by respiration or photosynthesis. Alternatively, a supply of energy could be derived from a blue light-absorbing pigment, independent of photosynthetic phosphorylation (§ 2.1).

The unequivocal demonstration that guard cells have adenosine triphosphatase (ATPase) activity associated with them would be a significant step in our understanding of the energetics of ion transport. These enzymes are normally bound to membranes and are believed to act as energy transfer agents for the transport of ions; metabolic energy may be supplied to membrane transport processes directly *via* the hydrolysis of ATP, catalysed by ATPase:

$$\text{ATP and } H_2O \underset{\textit{synthesis}}{\overset{\textit{hydrolysis}}{\rightleftharpoons}} \text{ADP and inorganic phosphate and free energy}$$

Although membrane-bound Mg^{2+} -activated/K^+ -stimulated ATPase activity has been demonstrated in the leaf epidermis of several species, there is as yet no direct evidence to implicate this enzyme in K^+ transport into the guard cells, however, its activity is altered by treatment of the epidermis with abscisic acid, which induces stomatal closure (§ 6.2).

Ultrastructural studies clearly indicate that mitochondria exist in large numbers within guard cells; the ratio of mitochondria to chloroplasts often exceeds the ratio in the mesophyll several-fold. Guard cells also contain demonstrable dehydrogenase activity and inhibitors of respiratory activity such as azide, cyanide and 2, 4,dinitrophenol (DNP) also inhibit stomatal opening. This evidence suggests that respiratory activity is one of the major sources of ATP within the guard cells. Similarly, studies utilizing inhibitors of photosynthetic phosphorylation indicate that ATP produced in this process is utilized in the stomatal mechanism. Dichlorophenyl-dimethyl urea, an inhibitor of non-cyclic photophosphorylation has no effect on stomatal opening under light and carbon dioxide-free conditions, whereas salicylaldoxime, an inhibitor of cyclic photophosphorylation suppresses light-stimulated opening, which cannot be reversed by carbon dioxide-free air. Similar results have been obtained using DNP, which in addition to inhibiting oxidative phosphorylation also inhibits cyclic photophosphorylation. Therefore, K^+ transport appears to require a supply of energy from photosystem I or cyclic photophosphorylation.

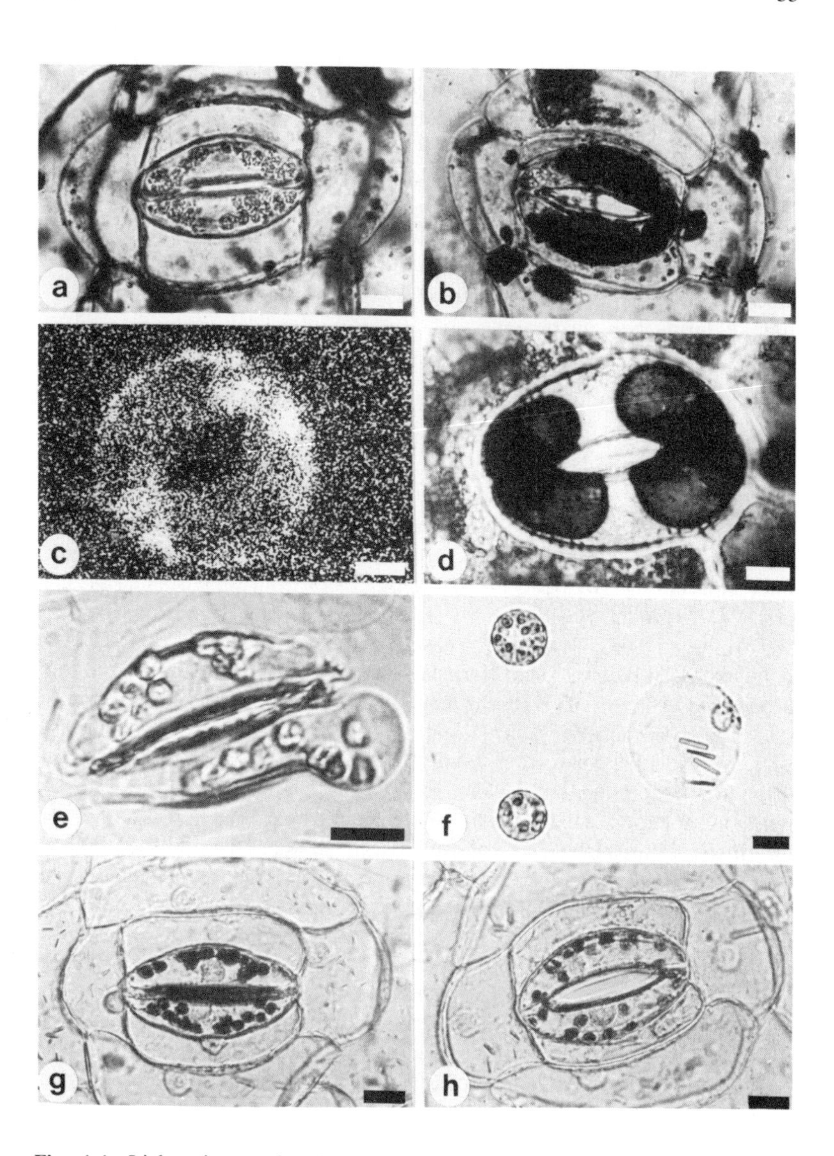

Fig. 4-4 Light micrographs of guard cells; the bars represent 10 μm. (**a**) and (**b**) Cobaltinitrite stain for potassium in closed (**a**) and open (**b**) guard cells of *Commelina communis*. (**c**) X-ray map of potassium in open guard cell complex of *Vicia faba*. (**d**) substomatal ion-adsorbent bodies in *Polypodium vulgare*. (**e**) and (**f**) guard cell protoplasts of *Commelina communis*, protoplast emerging from guard cell (**e**) and two guard cell and one epidermal cell protoplast (**f**). (**g**) and (**h**) starch inclusions in closed (**g**) and open (**h**) guard cells of *Commelina communis*.

The involvement of a blue light photoreceptor in ion transport in guard cells is even more speculative, although there is evidence that blue-absorbing pigments are located in or closely adjacent to the guard cell tonoplast, where they could exert a significant influence on ion transport into the vacuole. The chemical identity of the blue light photoreceptors is not yet known, although it may be a flavin-type compound, similar to other blue light photoreceptors found in the plant kingdom. These flavins may undergo photochemical reactions in blue light, the result of which is an 'excited' triplet state of the molecule. The decay of this excited triplet state could initiate a series of electron transfers which generate an electrochemical gradient to drive K^+ uptake during stomatal opening.

4.4 The chemiosmotic hypothesis of ion transport into guard cells

Currently we are far from understanding how the energy derived from the metabolism of respiratory substrates or from the excitation of chlorophylls or flavins is coupled to ion transport in guard cells. We can speculate on possible mechanisms by drawing parallels with other well researched systems, such as isolated mitochondria or chloroplasts. The chemiosmotic hypothesis of phosphorylation developed by MITCHELL (1966) from such isolated systems provides a model which can be extrapolated to guard cell ion tranport. According to this hypothesis, electron transport during respiration or photosynthesis is coupled to H^+ transport across the membranes which contain the electron carriers. This results in a concentration gradient of H^+ across the membrane, because it is virtually impermeable to protons (see TRIBE and WHITTAKER, 1982 for further details). This gradient can then be utilized to drive an H^+ transporting ATPase in the direction of ATP synthesis. These reactions appear to take place in the cristae membranes of mitochondria and the thylakoid membranes of chloroplasts, however, in the event that energy coupling does not take place, the energy derived from the proton gradient (the proton motive force) could be utilized in ion transport.

ZEIGER, BLOOM and HEPLER (1978), have recently suggested how the proton motive force might be utilized for ion transport in guard cells. They proposed that two distinct gradients exist as a result of the redox reactions taking place within the membrane: (*i*) an electrical gradient such that the interior of the guard cell becomes more negative. In fact there is experimental evidence which justifies the existence of this electrical gradient; intracellular electrical recordings indicate that in the light the guard cells hyperpolarize, i.e. become more negative inside, and they depolarize in darkness. As a consequence of this gradient, K^+ ions could move passively into the guard cells in order to dissipate the electrical gradient. (*ii*) A pH gradient exists such that there are more H^+ outside the guard cells and more OH^- inside. Evidence for the existence of a pH gradient has already been discussed (§ 4.2). As a consequence of this second gradient the guard cells may extrude OH^- and take up Cl^- to balance K^+ uptake. The net outcome of these changes would be that both H^+ and OH^- ions are pumped out and KCl is taken up by the guard cells. Therefore the primary transport process is the initial separation of H^+/OH^- in the membrane. Currently there is no evidence that this separation takes place because neither ATPases nor electron carriers have been demonstrated in the membranes of guard cells. Apart from this limitation, this hypothesis can explain many aspects of stomatal behaviour. In light a proton motive force could be generated by ATP production arising from photophosphorylation in the chloroplast or through a blue light photoreceptor inducing redox reactions within the tonoplast (or plasmalemma). Similarly in darkness a proton motive force could be generated by oxidative phosphorylation. In this hypothesis Cl^- acts as the initial counter ion to balance K^+ uptake, but Cl^- is often only present in small quantities within the guard cells, so that additional counter ions must be generated to maintain electroneutrality. Evidence that these could be organic anions is discussed in the following chapter.

5 Carbon Metabolism in Guard Cells

Early interest in the carbon metabolism of guard cells centred on the mechanism of starch-sugar changes and the possible photosynthetic activity of guard cell chloroplasts. However, more recent work has emphasised malate metabolism linking it with the role of potassium ions as an osmoticum for stomatal opening.

5.1 The role and metabolism of malate in guard cells

The decrease in osmotic potential which leads to stomatal opening can be attributed to an increase in the potassium ion concentration of the guard cells (§ 4.1). The potassium ions are taken up from elsewhere in the leaf or in an experimental situation from the surrounding solution. In order to maintain electroneutrality in the cell it is necessary to postulate that there must be either (*i*) an uptake of inorganic anions or a synthesis of organic anions, or (*ii*) an efflux of an osmotically inactive cation, e.g. H^+. In the majority of species so far studied, only a small proportion of the K^+ entering the guard cells seems to be counterbalanced by inorganic anions (§ 4.1). It was therefore, a major advance in the search for an additional method of achieving electroneutrality when ALLAWAY discovered in 1973 that about 50% of the K^+ taken up by *Vicia faba* guard cells, could be balanced by malate, providing that this organic anion existed in the divalent state. Subsequent studies using the same species demonstrated that the guard cells could accumulate sufficient malate and citrate to balance approximately two-thirds of the K^+ taken up.

The alternative method of achieving electroneutrality mentioned above is the efflux of an osmotically-inactive cation, such as H^+, in exchange for K^+. These protons could be provided if the guard cells are capable of synthesizing organic acids, because in the conversion of starch to malate two protons become available. One proton is released in the hydrolysis of carbon dioxide to carbonic acid, and another during the glycolytic oxidation of glyceraldehyde-3-phosphate to 1,3-diphosphoglyceric acid. Therefore, the biosynthesis of malate may have a dual role in the guard cells, producing both K^+ counterbalancing anions and protons.

On the evidence at present available it is difficult to say if there is a single mechanism for the maintenance of electroneutrality, however, the involvement of malate in this mechanism is clearly shown by the close correlation between epidermal malate levels and stomatal opening (Fig. 5-1).

The source of malate has been a subject of major inquiry over the past decade. Theoretically, malate could be transported from the mesophyll or adjacent epidermal cells or alternatively it could be synthesized inside the

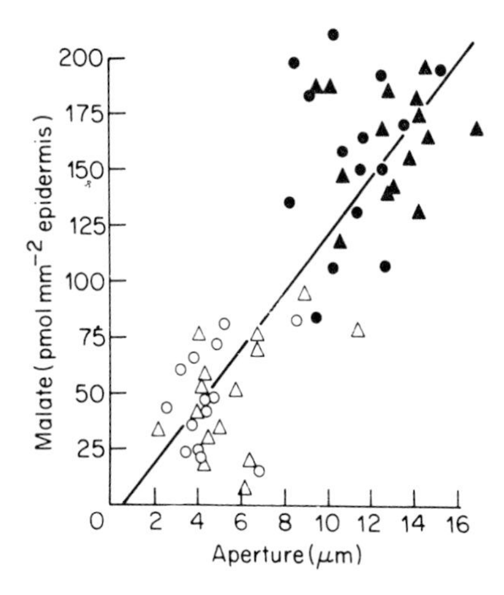

Fig. 5-1 A correlation between total epidermal malate and stomatal aperture. Each point is the total epidermal malate plotted against the mean aperture of 30 stomata from a single experiment. The different symbols represent different treatments which alter stomatal aperture (redrawn from TRAVIS and MANSFIELD (1977).

guard cells. Some early experiments demonstrated that in the epidermis of *Commelina communis*, the levels of malate and potassium did not change during stomatal movements. These results implied that malate was transported from adjacent epidermal cells, and led Bowling to propose the ingenious 'malate-switch' hypothesis to explain the mechanism of stomatal opening (BOWLING, 1976). However, there is now little evidence to support the 'malate-switch' hypothesis because studies with 'isolated' guard cells (§ 4.1) show that in several species malate can be synthesized within the guard cell.

One of the major biochemical mechanisms for malate synthesis in plant cells is *via* the enzyme phosphoenolpyruvate carboxylase (PEP carboxylase) which catalyses reaction (1) below:

(1) Phosphoenolpyruvate (PEP) + HCO_3^- → Oxaloacetate + Phosphate

Oxaloacetate can be rapidly reduced to malate by the enzyme malate dehydrogenase:

(2) Oxaloacetate + NADH (or NADPH) ⇋ Malate + NAD (or NADP)

WILLMER *et al.* (1973) found high levels of PEP carboxylase and malate dehyrogenase activity in extracts of epidermis from *Commelina communis* and *Tulipa gesneriana* (tulip), providing the first evidence that malate synthesis in the guard cells could take place by PEP carboxylation. They argued that PEP carboxylase was located primarily in the guard cells in the epidermis of *Commelina*, because they found that the activity of the enzyme was proportional to the frequency of stomata on the upper and lower epidermes.

This view has also been supported by detailed analytical studies of PEP carboxylase activity in isolated guard cells pairs of *Vicia faba*, although in this species high activity is also associated with the epidermal cells.

Malate synthesis requires a ready supply of the substrates PEP and carbon dioxide (or HCO_3^-, which is the true substrate of PEP carboxylase). The most likely source of PEP is from the breakdown of starch which is stored in the guard cell chloroplasts (§ 5.2). Early workers believed that the starch was synthesized from precursors, specifically, glucose-1-phosphate, transported from the mesophyll. However, the current concensus is that starch synthesis occurs by the reversal of glycolysis. The glycolytic pathway from starch to pyruvate is fully reversible, but because of thermodynamic considerations the conversion of malate to PEP by PEP carboxylase is not possible. In guard cell metabolism the steps from malate to PEP are very important for the regeneration of the substrate of PEP carboxylase or the reformation of starch during stomatal closure, yet these steps have proved to be the most difficult to elucidate.

Certain succulent plants, which accumulate malate in their mesophyll cells during the night and carry out Crassulacean Acid Metabolism overcome this problem of malate to PEP conversion in one of two ways: (*i*) by converting oxaloacetate to PEP with the enzyme PEP carboxykinase in the following reaction:

$$\text{Oxaloacetate} + \text{ATP} \rightarrow \text{PEP} + CO_2 + \text{ADP}$$

(*ii*) by decarboxylating malate with malic enzyme:

$$\text{Malate} \rightarrow CO_2 + \text{pyruvate}$$

The pyruvate is then converted to PEP by the enzyme pyruvate phosphate dikinase:

$$\text{Pyruvate} + \text{ATP} \rightarrow \text{PEP} + \text{AMP} + \text{PPi}$$

Although reversal of glycolysis has been clearly demonstrated in the guard cells of *Vicia faba*, the precise pathway of conversion is more difficult to define. Detailed studies of the enzyme complements may eventually lead to the elucidation of the pathway in guard cells. At present however, there are no reports of PEP carboxykinase in guard cells, while evidence for pyruvate phosphate dikinase in epidermis of *Vicia faba* is controversial.

Any biochemical mechanism which is used to explain malate production in guard cells must also be able to account for the observed enviromental effects of light and carbon dioxide on stomata. This is particularly important with respect to the known carbon dioxide effect on stomata (§ 2.2) which may pose a paradox in relation to malate production *via* PEP carboxylase. Low carbon dioxide levels are known to increase stomatal opening and malate production in epidermis, while increased carbon dioxide levels cause stomatal closure and a decrease in malate production; this is difficult to reconcile in view of the fact that carbon dioxide (as HCO_3^-) acts as a substrate for PEP carboxylase. This need not be a major obstacle to our understanding of the role of PEP carboxylase, since it is quite possible that an internal source of carbon dioxide is available for PEP carboxylation, should there be a limiting supply from the atmosphere. However, the possibility that carbon dioxide concentration exerts a controlling influence on stomatal aperture *via* PEP carboxylase is much more difficult to accept. Recently *in vitro* experiments have been carried out using the fungal toxin fusicoccin which is known to increase the rate of proton extrusion in many types of plant cell. These experiments have revealed that fusicoccin can reverse the normal response of stomata to carbon dioxide concentration while greatly stimulating stomatal opening and increasing malate production (Fig. 5-2). These unique studies imply that the control of stomatal opening by carbon dioxide concentration is independent of PEP carboxylation from an external source of carbon dioxide and therefore carbon dioxide concentration appears to exert its effect directly on ion transport processes.

There is now convincing evidence that malate synthesis takes place in the guard cells of many species during stomatal opening. However, the metabolic

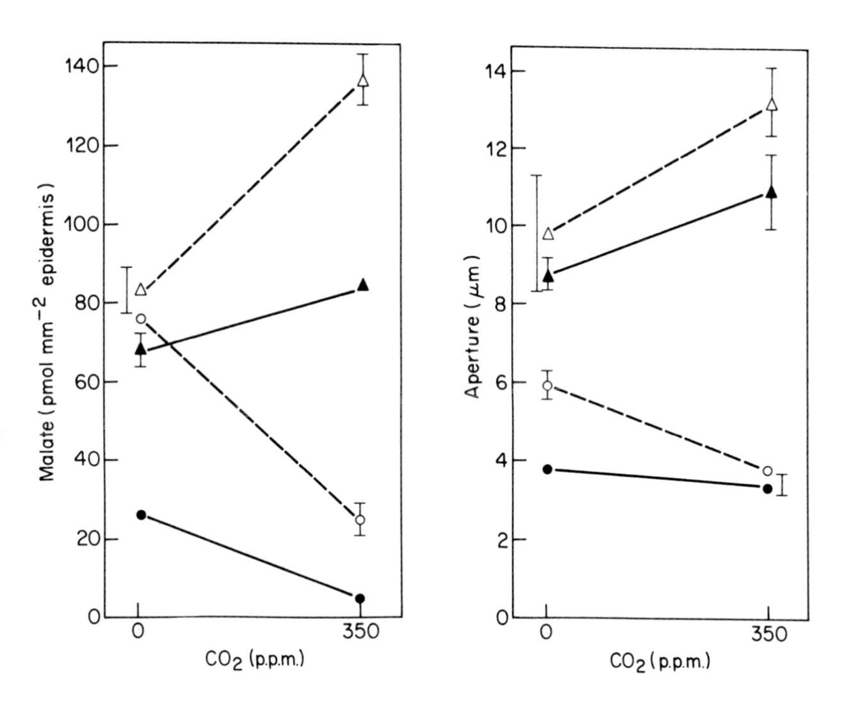

Fig. 5-2 The effect of fusicoccin on stomatal responses and epidermal malate levels to carbon dioxide. Each point is the mean of three replicate experiments. The bars represent +/− the standard error for three observations. ● dark −fusicoccin; ○ light −fusicoccin ▲ dark +fusicoccin; △ light +fusicoccin (redrawn from TRAVIS and MANSFIELD, 1979). N.B. The lines in this figure only link related points.

steps which take place during stomatal closure are less clearly understood. In order to close, the guard cells must dispose of their accumulated ions to reduce their turgor. Inorganic ions probably disperse in the apoplast of the guard cells and surrounding tissues, whereas malate may be disposed of in a variety of ways. These include: (*i*) catabolism in the tricarboxylic acid cycle, (*ii*) decarboxylation followed by reversal of glycolysis and (*iii*) efflux of malate into the surrounding cells. It has been demonstrated that all three pathways could operate in the epidermis of *Commelina communis*, although it seems likely that the third mechanism could allow the guard cells to reduce their turgor faster than the metabolic alternatives would allow. Some of the pathways of malate removal, along with the pathways of synthesis are outlined in Fig. 5-3.

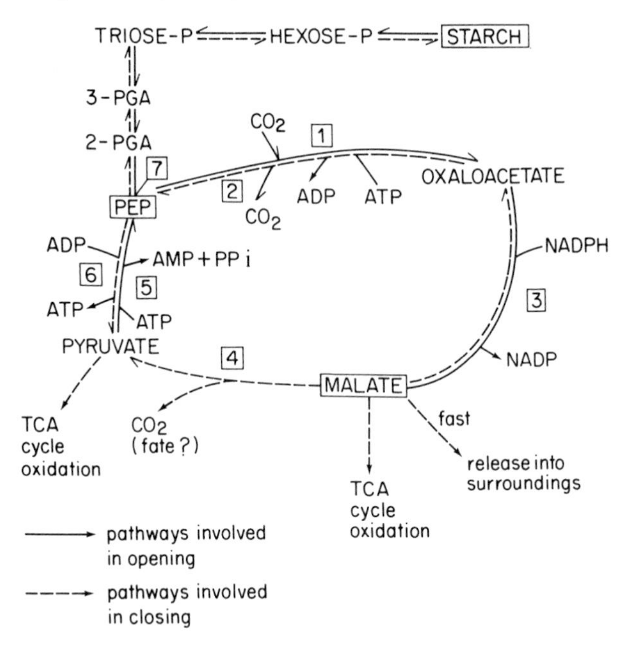

Fig. 5-3 Possible pathways involved in stomatal opening and closing. PGA, phosphoglyceric acid; PEP, phosphoenolpyruvate; ADP, adenosine diphosphate; ATP, adenosine triphosphate; TCA, tricarboxylic acid cycle. 1 PEP carboxylase; 2 PEP carboxykinase; 3 malate dehydrogenase; 4 malic enzyme; 5 pyruvate dikinase; 6 pyruvate kinase; 7 enolase (redrawn from MARTIN, DONKIN and STEVENS, 1982).

It has been suggested that the regulation of these pathways in the guard cell cytoplasm could be by the balance between carboxylation and decarboxylation; this could be brought about in several ways:

(*i*) feedback inhibition of PEP carboxylase by malate
(*ii*) pH dependence of PEP carboxylase and malic enzymes (low pH inhibits PEP carboxylase activity, while that of malic enzyme is increased)

(*iii*) availability of PEP may be controlled by starch mobilization and regulation of key enzymes of glycolysis

(*iv*) the balance between carboxylation and decarboxylation may be influenced by movement of K^+ and malate into the vacuole.

Regulatory mechanisms such as these are known to occur in the mesophyll cells of some succulent plants which accumulate malate to a high level, and similar mechanisms may operate in the guard cells, since they also accumulate malate up to levels of 100 mol m^{-3} or more.

Although malate would appear to be of major importance as a counter ion to K^+ in most species, there are some notable exceptions (especially some *Allium* spp.) in which the guard cell chloroplasts do not store starch. In this case malate appears to be replaced by Cl^- when an adequate supply is available from the soil. However, even though the malate level does not increase on stomatal opening small amounts of malate are still present in the guard cells. It is possible that the carbon required for the synthesis of this malate is transported from the mesophyll of the leaf. Alternatively, *Allium* guard cells contain soluble carbohydrate polymers such as fructosans which may provide another source of carbon for malate synthesis.

In plants which do contain starch in their guard cells the presence of high levels of chloride in the soil or in the case of epidermal tissue, in the incubation medium, causes a reduction in the epidermal malate levels and a breakdown of the correlation between malate and aperture. It is therefore difficult to say whether malate or Cl^- are individually essential. The level of chloride in the whole plant must also play an important role in determining which anion is responsible for maintaining electroneutrality.

5.2 Starch-sugar conversion

Starch commonly occurs in the plastids of stomatal guard cells even when it is absent from the rest of the leaf, for example, starch will persist in the guard cells of *Iris* after five weeks in complete darkness. Starch metabolism could therefore play a central role in stomatal movements. Working with the desert plant, *Verbena ciliata*, LLOYD (1908) found a diurnal rhythm in the starch contents of the guard cells, which he correlated with stomatal movement. He believed that the main cause of opening was an enzymatic digestion of starch, and he attributed closure during the afternoon or in darkness to removal of osmotic substances by the re-synthesis of starch .

SAYRE (1923) found a similar diurnal rhythm in guard cell starch content of *Rumex patientia* (patience dock) and also an inverse change in reducing sugars. He estimated that the latter were approximately twice as abundant in stomata open in the morning as those closed at night, however, there was not always an exact correlation of stomatal movements with these changes. In subsequent studies Sayre found that guard cells of open stomata showed a higher pH than those of closed stomata and this led him to propose that the effect of light was to bring about an increase in the pH of the guard cells either by oxidation of organic acids to carbon dioxide and water, or by removal of respiratory carbon dioxide by photosynthesis. He suggested that an increase in pH could cause an increase in the activity of starch hydrolysing enzymes which would induce the conversion of starch to sugar, causing the osmotic potential in the guard cell to decrease and the stomata to open. In 1940 an enzyme called phosphorylase, which carried out the following reaction, was discovered in potato tissue:

$$\text{Starch (amylose)} + \text{Inorganic phosphate} \rightleftharpoons \text{Glucose-1-phosphate}$$

This enzyme had an equilibrium point which moved towards the left (starch) at lower pH and to the right at higher pH, and it could therefore, be tenuously linked with starch breakdown in guard cells. It was later found that the enzyme phosphorylase does occur in guard cells. However, the breakdown of starch by this mechanism has the disadvantage that it involves no change in osmotic potential, since starch is insoluble and one molecule of glucose-1-phosphate is produced for one of inorganic phosphate consumed. For a change in osmotic potential to take place, enzymes must be present to breakdown glucose-1-phosphate.

Despite this difficulty, for a considerable period of time there was general acceptance of the hypothesis that light-induced stomatal movements were due to turgor changes brought about by a starch-sugar mechanism. Although a century has passed since this hypothesis was first formulated its relevance to the stomatal mechanism is still in doubt. Current thought and evidence links starch in guard cells with the production of PEP by glycolysis as a substrate for PEP carboxylase and with malate formation (§ 5.1). This does not however, exclude a secondary role for starch in the production of sugars. Starch could form an insoluble but relatively mobile pool of carbon in the guard cells, which may be shunted into one or other metabolite as required.

More recently analytical techniques have been developed which enable starch to be measured in guard cells much more accurately than was previously possible using histochemical techniques. These sensitive microanalytical procedures can measure nano- (10^{-9}) or pico- (10^{-12}) mole quantities of metabolites in single guard cell pairs of *Vicia faba*, and they have shown for the first time that there is a definite quantitative correlation between guard cell starch and stomatal aperture. These methods also show that reductions in starch during stomatal opening can account for all the malate synthesized, making transport from the mesophyll unnecessary.

The decrease in starch with stomatal opening seems to be well established (Fig. 4-4 g and h) but the concomitant increase in sugars is more controversial. Some workers have found no differences in sugar content of epidermal tissue with stomatal aperture, whereas others have found changes in glucose or sucrose which could be correlated with aperture. These discrepancies may be due to differences in technique or due to the stomatal mechanism itself. It may be that starch $\longleftrightarrow$ malate changes are most important during the opening or closing phases but that starch to sugar changes are associated with the open stomata to help maintain turgor in the guard cells. These sugars may not be removed immediately on closing but may remain in the guard cells to be metabolised during the night. The possible pathways involved are shown in Fig. 5–4.

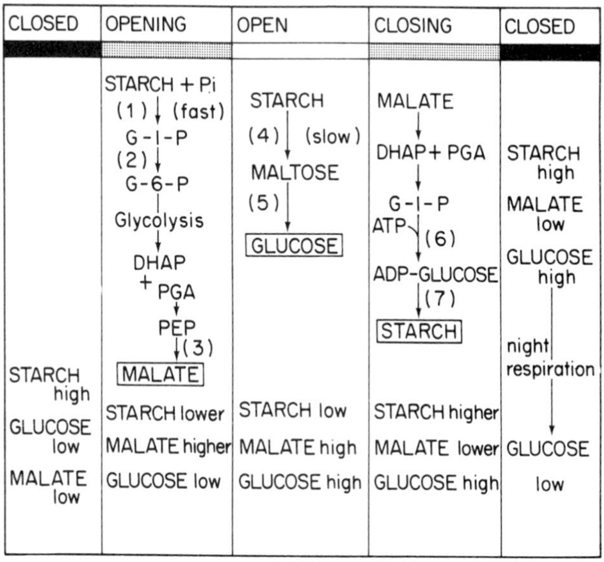

CLOSED	OPENING	OPEN	CLOSING	CLOSED
	STARCH + Pi (1) ↓ (fast) G-1-P (2) ↓ G-6-P ↓ Glycolysis ↓ DHAP + PGA ↓ PEP ↓ (3) MALATE	STARCH (4) ↓ (slow) MALTOSE (5) ↓ GLUCOSE	MALATE ↓ DHAP + PGA ↓ G-1-P ATP ↓ (6) ADP-GLUCOSE ↓ (7) STARCH	STARCH high MALATE low GLUCOSE high ↓ night respiration ↓
STARCH high GLUCOSE low MALATE low	STARCH lower MALATE higher GLUCOSE low	STARCH low MALATE high GLUCOSE high	STARCH higher MALATE lower GLUCOSE high	GLUCOSE low

Fig. 5-4 Diagram showing possible pathways of starch, glucose and malate metabolism at different stages of stomatal opening, The numbers in brackets refer to the following enzymes: (1) phosphorylase; (2) phosphoglucomutase; (3) PEP carboxylase and malate dehydrogenase; (4) α and β amylase; (5) maltase; (6) ADP-glucose pyrophosphorylase; (7) starch synthase; DHAP, dihydroxyacetone phosphate (after DONKIN and MARTIN, 1980).

Although the starch-sugar hypothesis cannot be accepted in its original form it is possible that a modification of the hypothesis may be used to explain cytoplasmic osmotic control. It seems likely that some form of osmotic substance in the cytoplasm regulates the osmotic concentration to match that of the vacuole; sugars produced from starch could fulfil this role.

5.3 The Calvin cycle and guard cell chloroplasts

Guard cells of most species contain chloroplasts, the role of which is not clearly understood. In C_3 plants the chloroplasts carry out a series of reactions known as the Calvin cycle (HALL and RAO, 1981). A key enzyme involved in the Calvin cycle is ribulose bisphosphate carboxylase (RuBP carboxylase) which catalyses the fixation of carbon dioxide into phosphoglyceric acid. In the early 1970s RUBP carboxylase activity was found in the epidermis of a variety of species, which implied that the Calvin cycle could operate in guard cells. However, more recent work has led to the opinion that these early results were due to unavoidable contamination of the epidermal tissue with mesophyll cell chloroplasts. More recently, ^{14}C labelling studies have shown that the Calvin cycle does not appear to operate in the epidermis of *Allium cepa* since no radioactivity was found in phosphoglyceric acid or sugar phosphates. At approximately the same time independent studies have shown that the epidermis of *Commelina communis* cannot catalyse the conversion of exogenous ribose-5-phosphate to ribulose-bisphosphate, indicating the absence of yet another Calvin cycle enzyme, phosphoribulokinase. Sensitive microanalytical techniques on single guard cell pairs of *Vicia faba* or *Nicotiana tabaccum* (tobacco) together with immunoelectrophoresis studies, were unable to detect RuBP carboxylase and only trace amounts of phosphoribulokinase and glyceraldehyde-3-P dehydrogenase. If, as this work seems to confirm, the Calvin cycle is absent from the guard cells of several species, then what is the precise function of the guard cell chloroplasts?

One function of the guard cell chloroplasts seems to be to store starch, but if these chloroplasts are simply a reservoir of starch, then why do they contain chlorophyll and organized membrane systems? The proposal that both photosystem I and II are present is still controversial. However, if it can be shown that guard cell chloroplasts do contain both photosystems but no Calvin cycle activity this would make them very unusual among plastid containing cells, the nearest example would be the mesophyll cells of C_4 plants which reduce phosphoglyceric acid as the Hill oxidant and carry out non-cyclic electron flow.

An additional complication can be found in certain species of *Paphiopedilum* and *Pelargonium zonale*, (geranium) which do not contain any chloroplasts in their guard cells, yet their stomata are functional. Chloroplasts may not therefore be essential for normal stomatal functioning in all species, but where they are present, they may act by producing ATP and reducing power (NADPH) for ion transport and other essential metabolic processes.

5.4 Transfer of metabolites to and from guard cells

If the Calvin cycle is absent from guard cells there will be no net fixation of carbon dioxide. The Calvin cycle is 'autocatalytic' which means that it provides the five carbon acceptor molecule RuBP for the fixation of carbon dioxide, as well as producing a C_3 sugar as product; no other pathway for carbon dioxide fixation can do this. So although there may be a metabolic cycle in guard cells in which starch is converted to malate and *vice versa* (Fig. 5-4) involving carbon dioxide fixation by PEP carboxylase, there is no net carbon dioxide fixation because the fixed carbon dioxide is removed during the decarboxylation step by malic enzyme. If guard cells cannot fix net carbon, in order to survive, they must import carbon from the rest of the leaf. There are certain lines of evidence to suggest that this can occur:

(*i*) Rates of carbon dioxide fixation are much higher in attached epidermis (epidermis which still has one side remaining attached to the leaf) than in detached epidermis in all species studied so far.

(*ii*) Autoradiographs of attached epidermis fed with $^{14}CO_2$ usually show label localized throughout the epidermal tissue, while in detached epidermis exposed to $^{14}CO_2$, label is generally located over the stomata.

(*iii*) Various techniques show that a pulse of $^{14}CO_2$ fed to the leaf eventually reached the epidermis.

(*iv*) It is possible by measuring the ratio of two stable isotopes of carbon (^{13}C and ^{12}C) to determine the predominant type of metabolism taking place in a tissue (i.e. C_3 or C_4 metabolism). Experiments of this kind with epidermal tissue of *C. communis* show a ratio that is consistent with C_3 metabolism. Since the Calvin cycle is not thought to be present in guard cells of this species, this data indicates that transport of C_3 metabolites from the mesophyll must take place.

Apart from the movement of metabolites into the epidermis from the mesophyll their movement from guard cells to adjacent cells in the epidermis and mesophyll is also important. In early studies with incubation of epidermal strips on $H^{14}CO_3^-$ the possibility of efflux of metabolites out of the guard cells into the medium was not considered, later work however, showed that when stomata on epidermal strips of *C. communis* were induced to close quickly (by placing on abscisic acid solution) or slowly (by placing on water) only labelled malate was found in the medium. It was concluded from this study that a large proportion of malic acid synthesized in the guard cells was exported from these cells during stomatal closure as a means of rapidly reducing turgor (§ 5.1).

In conclusion it appears that import of carbon from the mesophyll to the epidermis does occur, as well as loss of metabolites from the guard cells into the surrounding cells. However, the absence of plasmodesmata between mature guard cells and adjacent cells must limit the speed and efficiency of this process.

6 Antitranspirants and Future Developments in Stomatal Research

6.1 The role of antitranspirants in drought resistance

In dry areas, which make up one-third of the Earth's land mass and support about one-sixth of the world's population, the problems of achieving maximum crop yields are enormous. Even in temperate climates, crop yields can be frequently reduced by drought. In the United Kingdom, the prolonged drought of 1975 – 76 was so severe that substantial yield reductions occurred in all our major crops. Some agronomists estimate that world-wide losses in yields arising from water stress probably exceed those from all other causes, including pests and pathogens combined. Crop physiologists have, therefore, become increasingly aware of the significant advantages that could be derived from controlling water loss from the stomatal pores when water supplies are limiting.

There are several possible approaches to reducing the rate of transpiration in plants. Some involve controlling the environment surrounding the crop. For example, the erection of windbreaks can substantially reduce water loss from the crop canopy. Alternatively, methods of reducing the input of solar radiation to the leaf surface have been employed. Radiation can be reduced by the application of reflective pigments to the leaf surface, although complications can arise since all the leaves within a canopy may not be subject to the same level of solar radiation (distal leaves may shade more basal ones). Unfortunately, many of these techniques are only of limited applicability and therefore research has been intensified over the past twenty years to develop chemicals which can be applied to crops to reduce transpiration under a much wider range of conditions. Such compounds have been given the general name – 'antitranspirants' – and to date there are two major groups of these compounds: stomatal inhibitors and film-forming compounds. The former consist of a wide range of synthetic substances (herbicides, fungicides, plant growth regulators) which induce stomatal closure by a direct effect on the stomatal mechanism, or indirectly by some effect on a process not directly linked to the stomatal apparatus (e.g. by elevating the internal carbon dioxide concentration of the leaf as a result of inhibiting the photosynthetic activity of the mesophyll). The second group of antitranspirants involve the application to the leaf surface of relatively inert films, made from diverse groups of materials (dimethyl silicones, polyethylene and wax emulsions). These films occlude the stomatal pore and reduce cuticular transpiration and they are one of the oldest recorded methods of reducing transpiration (Theophrastus, 300 B.C.).

One of several arguments against the use of antitranspirants is that the stomata of most crop plants close in response to water stress and consequently control their own internal water status. Why then bother to close or occlude the pores artificially? It is true that most plants have several defence strategies to control water loss; stomata can for example act as sensors, responding to the external humidity of the atmosphere and are capable of closing to protect the leaf from excessive water loss under dry conditions. However, such defence mechanisms may not always be entirely adequate, particularly when the supply of water from the soil becomes limiting. Also from a theoretical point of view there are occasions when the artificial closure of stomata can lead to enhanced water use efficiency.

Antitranspirants which induce stomatal closure have been widely researched, often through the random testing of many chemicals, although it has been argued recently that this may not be the ideal method of solving the problem of improving water use efficiency, especially in view of the physiological complexity of the stomatal mechanism. One of the more interesting chemicals which have been tested is acetylsalicylic acid (a salicylate), commonly known as aspirin. The presence of salicylates in plants is well known, and particularly high concentrations occur in willow and many other species. However, no physiological role has yet been ascribed to them, although in 1978 it was discovered that when low concentrations of aspirin were fed via the petiole to leaves, it caused stomatal closure and reduced transpiration. This novel discovery provides a scientific basis for the traditional hospital practice of adding aspirin to the water of cut flowers to preserve them longer. Many of the chemicals tested so far have complicated side effects, which only came to light after detailed research studies on their mode of action. In the 1960s one compound, the fungicide, phenylmercuric acetate, proved to be a very powerful antitranspirant, causing stomatal closure at very low doses and improving the water use efficiency of crops. Field trials indicated that it might also be of value in controlling transpiration in pine plantations. However, detailed studies on its mode of action revealed that in addition to closing the stomata it caused substantial physiological toxicity to both the guard cells and surrounding subsidiary cells and furthermore, it directly inhibited the photosynthetic activity of the mesophyll. These studies fundamentally undermined its use as an antitranspirant, and because of the increasing antipathy towards the application of toxic elements such as mercury to food crops, the investigation of such compounds has now ceased. These studies have not, however, been entirely wasteful, because they have highlighted the criteria that are necessary for the development of commercially acceptable antitranspirants. Ideally antitranspirants should fulfil the following criteria:

(*i*) They should be non-toxic to humans and other forms of life.

(*ii*) They should have low mobility within the plant, only exerting a specific action on the guard cells or the cells immediately surrounding them. Inhibitory effects on the mesophyll or elsewhere in the plant should be minimal.

(*iii*) They should cause no permanent damage to the stomatal mechanism or to the structure of the guard cells.

(*iv*) Their effect should persist for several weeks.

(*v*) They should be cost effective.

The use of antitranspirant films has also been widely researched, although even here results have generally been inconsistent. Some successful applications have been made to vines to delay the harvesting of grapes and improve their yield. Films have also been used successfully to prevent desiccation and mortality during the transplantation of trees, and they also improve the survival and rooting of cuttings. Varied success has been achieved by their application to increase the shelf life of cut flowers and in preserving fruit after harvest. It has also been suggested that their application could reduce smog damage and reports indicate that film antitranspirants could also lower the incidence of certain foliar pathogens and pests.

One of the major limitations of antitranspirant films is their selective permeability to water and carbon dioxide. From a practical point of view the permeability of the film to water vapour should be smaller or at least equal to its permeability to carbon dioxide, otherwise photosynthesis could be reduced far more than transpiration, with obvious effects on the production ratio. To date even the most successful formulations are more permeable to water vapour than to carbon dioxide by a factor of at least four times. Film structures which have the required selective permeabilities to water vapour and carbon dioxide do not yet exist. It is also essential that the films should be inexpensive, non-toxic, remain elastic for long periods and resist degradation by solar, UV radiation and micro-organisms. Currently, there appear to be too many constraints for the widespread implementation of film antitranspirants in agriculture, although their successful application in specific situations will no doubt continue.

6.2 Naturally-occurring antitranspirants

With one exception, all the inhibitors of stomatal transpiration which had been investigated up to 1970 were toxic. The sole exception was carbon dioxide. At elevated atmospheric levels of carbon dioxide stomata close and reduce transpiration, and concurrently photosynthesis increases because of the steeper carbon dioxide diffusion gradient into the leaf. In maize, for example, by raising the atmospheric carbon dioxide concentration by approximately 0.025% transpiration can be cut by 23% and net photosynthesis increased by 30%. However, the general application of this technology to field crops is questionable and its practical application may only be realized on crops grown in greenhouses and polythene tunnels, where the conservation of water may be of little significance.

The search for an ideal antitranspirant was considerably stimulated in 1969 by the discovery that the naturally-occurring plant growth inhibitor, abscisic acid (ABA) accumulated in the leaves of wheat after they had been subjected to water stress. One of the most significant physiological changes occurring in such stressed plants is the suppression of stomatal opening. Observations that low concentrations of externally applied ABA could simulate this response led to more detailed studies of the mode of action of ABA on the stomatal physiology of plants. Preliminary results showed that single surface application of ABA (0.02 μg cm^{-2} of leaf surface) could suppress stomatal opening for up to 9 days. At the same time it was found that young 'wilty' mutants of tomato, which were unable to close their stomata, were unable to synthesize ABA. It therefore seemed probable that endogenous ABA might be playing an important role both in the normal behaviour of stomata, as well as regulating their behaviour after water stress.

The mode of action of ABA on the stomatal mechanism is still rather uncertain although it seems to inhibit 70–80% of the K^+ uptake into the guard cells of some species, and recent evidence indicates that increased efflux of K^+ (estimated from $^{86}Rb^+$ efflux experiments) may be involved in ABA-induced stomatal closure. ABA treatments also inhibit starch breakdown within the guard cell chloroplasts and enhance the incorporation of glucose into guard cell starch. Measurements of the intercellular carbon dioxide concentration in ABA treated leaves indicate that although small increases occur they are insufficient to account for the substantial closure which is observed. The effects of externally applied ABA are very rapid, in some species stomatal closure is initiated within 2.6 minutes; in other species closure is initiated within 8-9 minutes and complete closure can be observed in 30 minutes. The mode of action of ABA therefore closely approaches the ideal characteristics of an antitranspirant which were outlined in the previous section and although it will reduce the overall growth of the plant, this may not be too detrimental during conditions of extreme water shortage. However, field trials, particularly on orchard trees and cereals, have not been too encouraging, since its effects are too short-lived to be of commercial interest. As a consequence future studies are likely to involve a search for chemical analogues of ABA which because they cannot be metabolized by the plant, have a more prolonged action. It has already been established that in some species the methyl ester of ABA can reduce transpiration for up to 9 days, possibly as a result of greater penetration into the plant or due to slower breakdown in the plant (Fig. 6-1). Such results are an optimistic sign that analogues with an appropriate action may be synthesized in the near future.

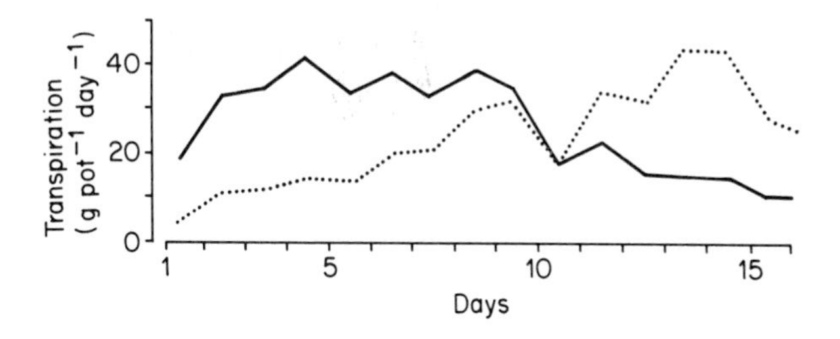

Fig. 6-1 The effect of the methyl ester of ABA on water loss of unwatered coffee plants. Untreated plants, (solid line) treated plants (dotted line) (redrawn from MANSFIELD, WELLBURN and MOREIRA (1978).

Future research may also involve other naturally occurring compounds which accumulate during wilting. Recent work at the University of Lancaster by Mansfield and co-workers has revealed that in water stressed sorghum, a sesquiterpenoid called all-*trans*-farnesol accumulates in the leaf material (Fig. 6-2). When this compound is applied externally to sorghum leaves it also induces stomatal closure, There is also evidence that phenolic acids such as scopoletin and chlorogenic acid which occur naturally as plant growth inhibitors and accumulate under various stress conditions, can also induce stomatal closure, Scopoletin and chlorogenic acid are believed to act as competitive inhibitors of the plant growth hormone indole-3-ylacetic acid (IAA) and recent reports that IAA may stimulate stomatal opening and antagonize the closing response to ABA may indicate a very complex interaction between various growth regulators during the development of water stress, and if we are to simulate this behaviour artificially we need to know much more about their mode of action on the stomatal mechanism.

6.3 Crop breeding and drought resistance

Shortage of water is already a major factor limiting crop yields in many parts of the world, therefore we need to develop breeding strategies to improve the drought resistance of many of our cultivated crops. Nowhere is this more imperative than in cereal crops, which provide the major source of food to the world's population.

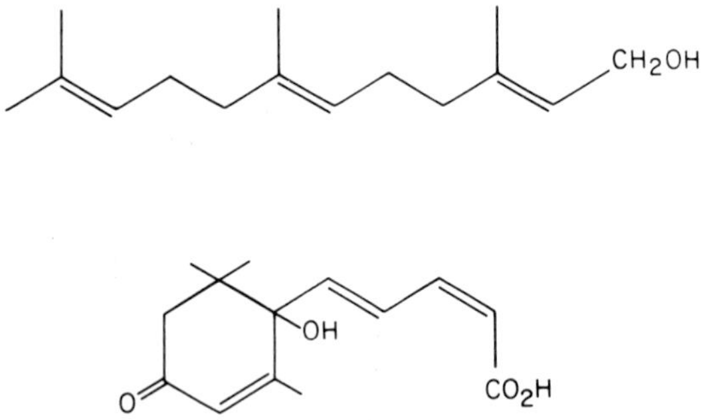

Fig. 6-2 Chemical structures of all-*trans*-farnesol (top) and abscisic acid (bottom).

Drought resistance is determined by a number of physiological and morphological characters. The control of water loss by the stomata is one character which many physiologists and plant breeders believe may provide a means of improving drought resistance. Reduced stomatal frequency (the number of stomata per unit area of leaf) is one selection criterion for drought resistance and there is evidence that this parameter can be associated with increased drought tolerance in cereal seedlings. However, the problem is more complex than this implies, because if reduced stomatal frequency is the only selection parameter utilized, then plants with lower numbers of stomata tend to compensate by producing larger leaves and larger stomata and their water use efficiency remains the same. Such results reveal how complicated plant breeding studies can be, although, they may open up new lines of inquiry, because it may be possible to reduce water use by selecting for low stomatal frequencies, coupled with the selection of other parameters, such as smaller stomata, smaller leaves or low stomatal index. Another interesting avenue of inquiry concerns the differences in drought-induced abscisic acid (ABA) accumulation which has been observed in several cereal varieties. ABA is a natural regulator of stomatal aperture (§ 6.2) and therefore intial selection might be made for different levels of ABA accumulation in response to stress, instead of for differences in stomatal response.

The identification of these morphological and physiological characters is of paramount importance in any plant breeding strategy, because it is only then possible to exploit such variation. Ultimately by their introduction into commercial varieties, it may be possible to maintain and even enhance the high yields that have been achieved in recent years.

7 Suggestions for Practical Work

7.1 Epidermal strip bioassays

Stomata respond rapidly to a wide range of environmental, osmotic and hormonal stimuli, they therefore appear to be ideal experimental subjects for plant physiological practicals. MANSFIELD (1971) has pointed out some of the difficulties which may be encountered in using stomata on the intact plant. These exercises use epidermal tissue, require little equipment and are suitable for undergraduate classes or advanced level classes in schools.

Epidermis can be obtained from the leaves of many plant species, e.g. *Vicia faba, Tradescantia* × *andersoniana, Nicotiana tabaccum,* but the dayflower (*Commelina communis*) is particularly well suited to these studies, since the epidermis can be removed from the leaves very easily with little mesophyll contamination.

The composition of the incubation medium has an important effect on the stomatal behaviour. There is evidence that epidermis of *Commelina communis* needs about 50 mol m^{-3} K^+ (usually KCl) in order to achieve optimal sensitivity to different environmental conditions. A useful general purpose incubation medium for epidermal strips is 10 mol m^{-3} MES (morpholino ethanesulphonic acid) adjusted to pH 6.15 (KOH) plus 50 mol m^{-3} KCl.

Strips of lower epidermis (5 × 10 mm) from *Commelina communis* may be easily detached by means of forceps and floated cuticle side up on distilled water. Any epidermis contaminated with mesophyll tissue should be discarded and the strips should be transferred as soon as possible to the incubation medium.

The incubation of strips may take place in 5 cm diameter Petri dishes containing 10 cm^3 of incubation medium. Air containing normal levels of carbon dioxide (+ CO_2) or air passed through a soda lime column (− CO_2) is bubbled through the solutions at a rate of 100 cm^3 min^{-1}. The dishes are incubated in a water bath at 25°C, illuminated from below for 3 h. Dark treatments may be obtained by wrapping the dishes in aluminium foil.

After incubation, the apertures of 10 stomata on each of 3 epidermal strips should be measured under the microscope, giving a total of 30 stomata per treatment. Results may then be analysed statistically using Analysis of Variance. Suggested experiments include: investigation of K^+ concentration on stomatal opening (usually in the range 0–200 mol m^{-3}), or investigation of the effect of abscisic acid by adding this to the incubation medium at 10^{-8} to 10^{-4} mol m^{-3}.

7.2 Histochemical localization of K^+ in guard cells

The accumulation of K^+ in guard cells can be demonstrated histochemically using the sodium cobaltinitrite stain (Macallum stain). The stain, which *must* be freshly made up, consists of 10 g of cobalt nitrate and 17.5 g sodium nitrite dissolved in 38 cm^3 of dilute acetic acid (1 part glacial in 7.5 parts distilled water). The stain must be prepared in a fume cupboard because the mixture gives off quantities of nitrogen dioxide, which must be purged from the solution by bubbling air slowly through the mixture for five minutes. The stain should be ice cold when it is used because the complex double salt, sodium potassium cobaltinitrite is insoluble in ice cold water. Excess sodium cobaltinitrite can be removed from the tissue by washing briefly with two changes of ice cold distilled water. Epidermis should be left for 30 min in the stain, washed, and then fixed in 5% ammonium sulphide (fume cupboard). A black deposit of cobalt sulphide is seen where the potassium was localized in the living tissue.

7.3 Malate determination in epidermis

Malate can be assayed in epidermal strips after incubation as described in section 7.1 or in strips taken directly from the plant. Malate is extracted from the strips by deproteinizing in 600 μl of 1 mol dm^{-3} $HClO_4$ for 30 min at room temperature. The sample is then centrifuged for 10 min at 2000 *g* and equal quantities of supernatant and 1 mol dm^{-3} K_2CO_3 are mixed. The neutralized extract is then centrifuged for 5 min at 4000 *g* and 450 μl of the supernatant is added to each of two cuvettes containing 600 μl of NAD-buffer mixture (3.33 mg NAD cm^{-3}, 0.4 mol dm^{-3} Hydrazine sulphate – CARE POISON!, 1 mol dm^{-3} glycine, 0.2% Na_2 EDTA, pH 9.5 (NaOH) adjusted immediately before use). 10 μl MDH (Malate dehydrogenase 1000 IU cm^{-3} in 1.5 mol dm^{-3} $(NH_4)_2SO_4$) is then added to one of the cuvettes and the malate content is calculated from the difference in absorbance at 340 nm between the two cuvettes after 30 min at room temperature.

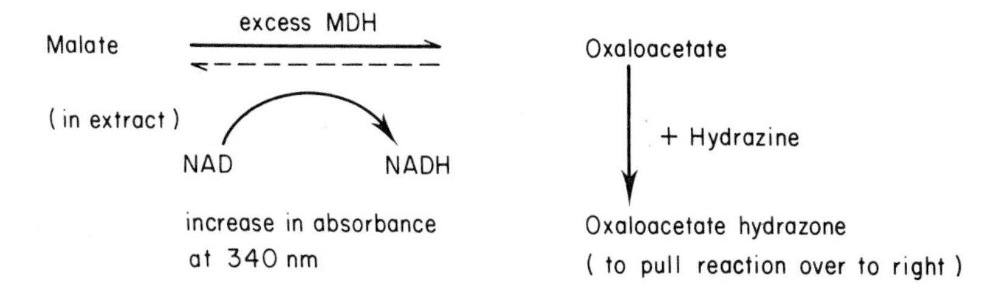

Malate can be measured in experiments such as those described in section 7.1

7.4 Preparation of guard cell protoplasts

Experimental work with guard cell protoplasts offers a new approach to the study of stomatal physiology. In using protoplasts the complicated problems encountered in isolation of guard cells on epidermal strips are avoided, and studies can also be made on the protoplast without effects due to the cell wall.

Mesophyll protoplasts have been prepared for many years for use in a variety of studies including, photosynthesis, development and genetics, however, it is only relatively recently that methods have been investigated for the isolation of guard cell protoplasts. One such method, developed by Fitzsimons and Weyers in Dundee has been adapted and is described here for the preparation of protoplasts from guard cells of *Commelina communis*.

(1) The concentration of mannitol required to *just* plasmolyse the guard cells of the *Commelina communis* plants is determined; this concentration is then used for subsequent incubations and media.

(2) Strips of lower epidermis are peeled from fully expanded leaves and floated on a suitable mannitol concentration (usually around 0.3 mol dm^{-3}).

(3) Usually 3 or 4 large Petri dishes of tissue are collected.

(4) The mannitol is then removed with a Pasteur pipette and replaced with enzyme solution which consists of: 4% Cellulysin (dialysed overnight) + 0.5% Bovine Serum Albumin 0.3 mol dm^{-3} mannitol in 10 mol m^{-3} MES buffer, adjusted to pH 5.0 with KOH.

(5) Lids are placed on the Petri dishes and they are incubated at 30°C for 3 h with *very gentle* agitation.

(6) At the end of the incubation period the strips can be inspected under the microscope to see if the protoplasts have been released. If not the incubation can be carried on for a longer time.

(7) The protoplasts are harvested by centrifugation at approximately 300 *g*, and the strips of epidermis are washed several times with mannitol solution to remove adhering protoplasts.

(8) To purify the guard cell protoplasts and separate them from any mesophyll or epidermal protoplasts, they may be layered carefully on a 0–90% Percoll gradient and centrifuged at approx. 400 *g* for 5 min. The guard cell protoplasts should separate out as a band distinct from the epidermal protoplasts and mesophyll protoplasts.

For exact details of mannitol or cellulysin concentrations, incubation times, and centrifugation speeds it is preferable to experiment with the equipment available and plant material.

To avoid damage to the protoplasts excessive shaking and pipetting through small apertures should be avoided. The size of the final protoplasts will be controlled by the mannitol concentration in which they are kept, however it is advisable not to go below 0.2 mol dm^{-3} since this may result in the protoplasts bursting. Once the purified protoplast preparation is obtained experiments may be carried out to determine the effects of ABA or fusicoccin on protoplast shrinkage or swelling.

References and Further Reading *

ALLAWAY, W.G. (1973). *Planta,* **110**, 63-70.

BARRS, H.D. (1971). *Annual Review of Plant Physiology,* **22**, 223-36.

BOWLING, D.J.F. (1976). *Nature* (London), **262**, 393-4.

BRADY, J. (1979). *Biological Clocks,* Studies in Biology, no. 104. Edward Arnold, London.

DARWIN, F. (1898). *Philosophical Transactions of the Royal Society, Series B,* **190**, 531-621.

DONKIN, M.E. and MARTIN, E.S. (1980). *Plant Cell Environment,* **3**, 409-14.

FISCHER, R.A. (1968). *Plant Physiology,* **43**, 1947-52.

FUJINO, M. (1967). *Science Bulletin, Faculty of Education,* Nagasaki University, **18**, 1-47.

GLINKA, Z. and MEIDNER, H. (1968). *Journal of Experimental Botany,* **19**, 152-66.

HALL, D.O. and RAO, K.K. (1981). *Photosynthesis,* 3rd edition, Studies in Biology, no. 37. Edward Arnold, London.

HEATH, O.V.S. (1950). *Journal of Experimental Botany,* **1**, 29-62.

* HEATH, O.V.S. (1981). *Stomata.* Carolina Biological Supply Company.

HEATH, O.V.S. and MEIDNER, H. (1961). *Journal of Experimental Botany,* **12**, 226-42.

HSIAO, T.C., ALLAWAY, W.G. and EVANS, L.T. (1973). *Plant Physiology,* **51**, 82-8.

HUMBLE, G.D. and HSIAO, T.C. (1969). *Plant Physiology,* **44**, 230-4.

KUIPER, P.J.C. (1964). *Plant Physiology,* **39**, 952-5.

LLOYD, F.E. (1908). *Publications. Carnegie Institute of Washington,* **82**, 1-142.

LOFTFIELD, J.V.G. (1921). *Publications. Carnegie Institute of Washington,* **314**, 1-104.

MANSFIELD, T.A. (1971). *Journal of Biological Education,* **5**, 115-23.

MANSFIELD, T.A. and HEATH, O.V.S. (1963). *Journal of Experimental Botany,* **14**, 334-52.

MANSFIELD, T.A. and MEIDNER, H. (1966). *Journal of Experimental Botany,* **17**, 510-52.

MANSFIELD, T.A., WELLBURN, A.R. and MOREIRA, T.J.S. (1978). *Philosophical Transactions of the Royal Society, London, Series B,* **284**, 471-82.

MARTIN, E.S. and MEIDNER, H. (1971). *New Phytologist,* **70**, 923-8.

MARTIN, E.S., DONKIN, M.E. and STEVENS, R.A. (1982). *School Science Review,* **63**, 459-68.

MEIDNER, H. (1975). *Journal of Experimental Botany,* **26**, 666-73.

MEIDNER, H. and HEATH, O.V.S. (1959). *Journal of Experimental Botany,* **10**, 206-19.

MEIDNER, H. and MANSFIELD, T.A. (1965). *Biological Reviews,* **40**, 483-509.

* MEIDNER, H. and MANSFIELD, T.A. (1968). *Physiology of Stomata.* McGraw Hill, Maidenhead.

MITCHELL, P. (1966). *Biological Reviews,* **41**, 445-502.

MOURAVIEFF, I. (1958). *Bulletin. Société botanique de France,* **105**, 467-75.

PENNY, M.G. and BOWLING, D.J.F. (1974). *Planta,* **119**, 17-25.

RASCHKE, K. and HUMBLE, G.D. (1973). *Planta,* **115**, 47-57.

SAYRE, B.D. (1923). *Science,* **57**, 205-6.

SCARTH, G.W., WHYTE, J. and BROWN, A. (1933). *Transactions of the Royal Society, Canada,* **51**, 115-17.

STALFELT, M.G. (1962). *Physiologia Plantarum,* **15**, 772-9.

* SUTCLIFFE, J. (1979). *Plants and Water,* 2nd edition, Studies in Biology no. 14. Edward Arnold, London.

TRAVIS, A.J. and MANSFIELD, T.A. (1977). *New Phytologist,* **78**, 541-6.

TRAVIS, A.J. and MANSFIELD, T.A. (1979). *New Phytologist,* **83**, 607-14.

TRIBE, M. and WHITTAKER, P. (1982). *Chloroplasts and Mitochondria,* 2nd edition, Studies in Biology, no. 31. Edward Arnold, London.

VIRGIN, M.I. (1956). *Physiologia Plantarum,* **9**, 482-92.

WILLMER, C.M., KANAI, R., PALLAS, J.E. Jr. and BLACK, C.C. Jr. (1973). *Life Science,* **12**, 151-5.

WRIGHT, S.T.C. and HIRON, R.W.P. (1969). *Nature* (London), **224**, 719-20.

ZEIGER, E., BLOOM, A.J. and HEPLER, P.K. (1978). *What's New in Plant Physiology,* **9**, 29-32.

N.B. Asterisk denotes Further Reading.

Index